Grade 1 Math

W9-CRI-083

Contents

Trace and print the numbers.

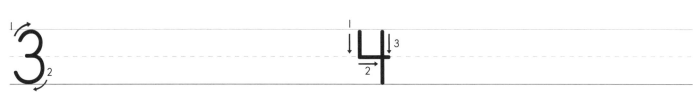

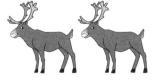

Count the items. Print the number on the line.

2

Written by teachers working in the Canadian classroom

Math

Canadian Curriculum Press
Forward Learning

Grade 1

10 − 4 =

4 × 8

- Counting to 100
- Addition, subtraction, beginning fractions
- Canadian money, time
- Shapes, symmetry, patterning
- And much more!

D. J. Whitlock, B.Ed.

Trace and print the numbers.

Count the items. Print the number on the line.

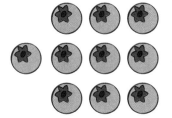

Example:

Count the items.

Circle the number.   ① 2 3 4 5

Count the items.

Circle the number.   1 2 3 4 5

Count the items.

Circle the number.   1 2 3 4 5

Count the items.

Circle the number.   1 2 3 4 5

Count the items.

Circle the number.   1 2 3 4 5

Count the items.

Circle the number.   1 2 3 4 5

Example: Count and draw the missing shapes.

8

10

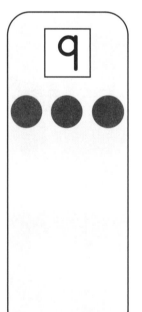

9

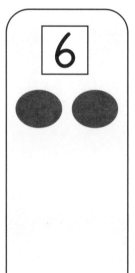

6

7

Say the number. Colour the matching number of squares or circles.

Example:

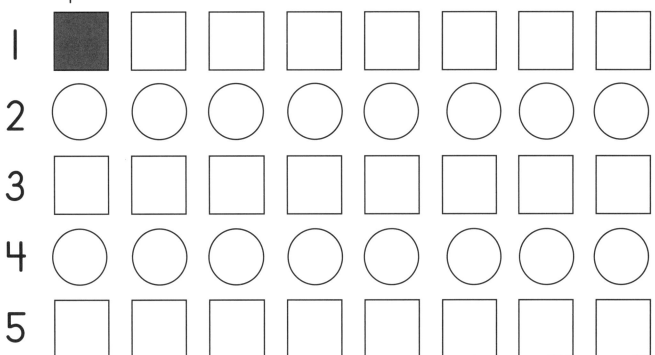

1
2
3
4
5

Say the number.

Circle the matching number of items.

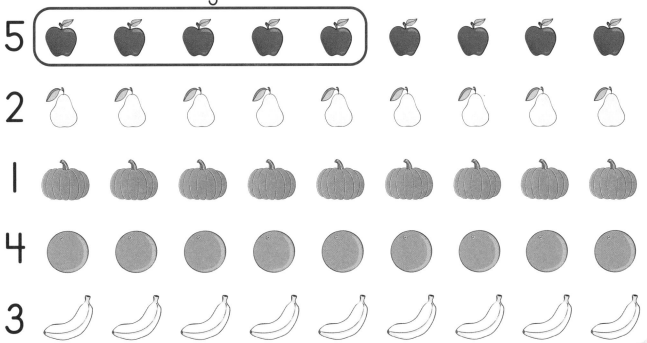

5
2
1
4
3

Draw a line from each word to the matching number.

Example:

three   5

five   1

two   3

six   6

one   2

Matching Number to Quantity

Count the maple leaves in each part of the beach towel.
Colour each part to match the numbered crayon.

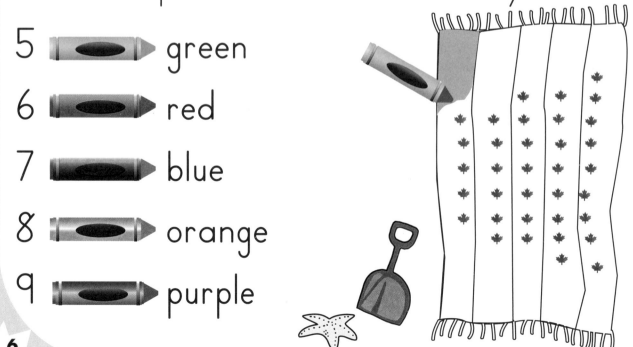

5 green

6 red

7 blue

8 orange

9 purple

Count the maple leaves. Fill in the blanks.

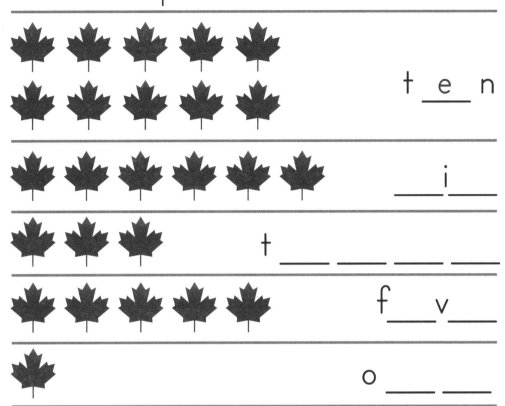

0	= zero
1	= one
2	= two
3	= three
4	= four
5	= five
6	= six
7	= seven
8	= eight
9	= nine
10	= ten

t _e_ n

___ i ___

t ___ ___ ___ ___

f ___ v ___

o ___ ___

e ___ g ___ ___

z ___ ___ ___

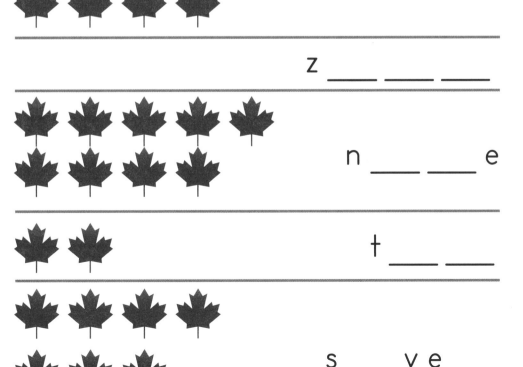

n ___ ___ e

t ___ ___

s ___ v e ___

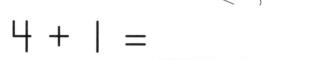

Add:

Example:

$$1 + 3 = \underline{\quad 4 \quad}$$
$$3 + 1 = \underline{\qquad}$$
$$2 + 2 = \underline{\qquad}$$
$$3 + 0 = \underline{\qquad}$$

$$4 + 1 = \underline{\qquad}$$
$$2 + 1 = \underline{\qquad}$$
$$3 + 2 = \underline{\qquad}$$
$$1 + 4 = \underline{\qquad}$$

Number and Quantity

Say each number.

Draw the matching number of objects in each box.

Example:

5 ○ ○ ○ ○ ○	7	4
8	6	9

Subtract. Try using counters to help.

2   3 ● ● ●   4 ● ● ● ●

$$\begin{array}{r} 2 \\ -1 \\ \hline 1 \end{array}$$
$$\begin{array}{r} 3 \\ -1 \\ \hline \end{array}$$
$$\begin{array}{r} 4 \\ -2 \\ \hline \end{array}$$

Draw your own counters for these ones.

$$\begin{array}{r} 5 \\ -3 \\ \hline \end{array}$$
$$\begin{array}{r} 4 \\ -3 \\ \hline \end{array}$$
$$\begin{array}{r} 3 \\ -3 \\ \hline \end{array}$$

Recording Numbers 1 to 50

Print missing numbers in the boxes.

1									10
									20
									30
									40
									50

Greater than   Less than

>   <

(Hint: The open side of the symbol points to the greater number.)

3 hotdogs

Which is greater?
3 is less than 5,
so we write:
3 < 5

5 hotdogs

Write the numbers and > or <.

___3__ ⊙ __2____

___ ◯ ___

___ ◯ ___

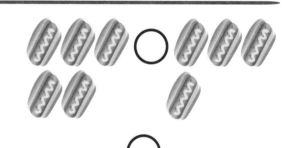

___ ◯ ___

Write > or < in the ◯. The number line can help.

9 ⊙ 2   4 ◯ 1   8 ◯ 7   2 ◯ 5

8 ◯ 5   1 ◯ 3   3 ◯ 5   6 ◯ 2

1 2 3 4 5 6 7 8 9 10

Add.

Example:

2 + 5 = __7__   1 + 5 = _____   4 + 3 = _____

1 + 6 = _____   6 + 2 = _____   0 + 8 = _____

5 + 3 = _____   2 + 7 = _____   3 + 4 = _____

7 + 1 = _____   1 + 8 = _____   6 + 3 = _____

4 + 5 = _____   3 + 7 = _____   5 + 5 = _____

Number Sequencing

Print the numbers that are missing.

1   2   3   4   5   _6_   ___   8

5   6   7   ___   ___   10   ___   ___

9   10   11   ___   ___   14   ___   16

15   ___   17   ___   ___   20   ___   22

22   ___   ___   ___   26   ___   ___   ___

Print the missing numbers.

1 2 3 __ __ 6 7 8 __ __ 11 12 __ __ 15

__ 17 18 __ __ 21 __ 23 24 __ __ 27 __ __

30 31 32 __ __ 35 __ 37 __ __ 40 __ 42 __

Addition to 10

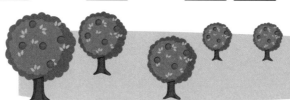

Add.

3	9	9	6	5	0	4	4	5	3
+5	+1	+2	+2	+5	+4	+5	+2	+4	+6

Number Sequencing

Print the number that goes before.

| 11 , 12, 13 | ___ ,7, 8 | ___ ,1,2 |

Print the number that goes between.

| 6, ___ , 8 | 9, ___ ,11 | 17, ___ ,19 |

Print the number that goes after.

| 8, 9, ___ | 14, 15, ___ | 18, 19, ___ |

12

Subtract.

8	5	9	9	9	6	9	5	8	7	7	6
-4	-4	-8	-6	-4	-3	-2	-3	-5	-3	-4	-4

Identifying Greater and Less

Circle the number that is greater.

(8) 6   17 20   18 16

Circle the number that is less.

21 (12)   18 14   8 0

Print missing numbers in the boxes.

51	52								
										100

Addition Facts

Add.

5	2	4	2	3	2
+1	+3	+1	+2	+2	+1
◯	◯	◯	◯	◯	◯

1	3	3	4	5	4
+4	+1	+4	+2	+0	+4
◯	◯	◯	◯	◯	◯

3	2	3	2	4
+0	+4	+5	+5	+5
◯	◯	◯	◯	◯

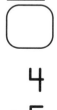

14

Print the missing numbers. Then touch each number and say it out loud.

1	2		4	5	6	7		9	10
11		13	14	15			18		
	22	23			26	27		29	
31		33	34		36		38		40
	42	43		45		47		49	
51			54	55			58		60
	62	63			66	67			
71			74	75			78	79	80
		83			86	87			90
91	92		94	95			98	99	

Subtraction Facts

Subtract.

$$\begin{array}{r} 6 \\ -1 \\ \hline \end{array} \qquad \begin{array}{r} 4 \\ -2 \\ \hline \end{array} \qquad \begin{array}{r} 3 \\ -1 \\ \hline \end{array} \qquad \begin{array}{r} 1 \\ -1 \\ \hline \end{array} \qquad \begin{array}{r} 5 \\ -2 \\ \hline \end{array} \qquad \begin{array}{r} 4 \\ -1 \\ \hline \end{array}$$

For each pair, circle the number that is more.
Example:

(23) 13	72 70	24 14
49 50	19 21	92 89

For each pair, circle the number that is less.
Example:

42 (24)	56 65	11 17
32 43	82 28	21 51

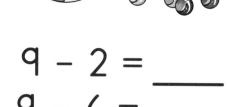

Subtraction Facts

Subtract.

$6 - 4 =$ _____ $10 - 4 =$ _____ $9 - 2 =$ _____

$8 - 4 =$ _____ $7 - 3 =$ _____ $9 - 6 =$ _____

$8 - 5 =$ _____ $9 - 3 =$ _____ $6 - 2 =$ _____

$7 - 5 =$ _____ $6 - 5 =$ _____ $7 - 1 =$ _____

$6 - 3 =$ _____ $9 - 0 =$ _____ $4 - 2 =$ _____

$7 - 4 =$ _____ $10 - 6 =$ _____ $8 - 2 =$ _____

Number Sense and Numeration - Place Value

For each set of base ten blocks, count the number of tens and ones and write it on the line.

 **equals 1 ten**   ▫ **equals 1 one**

___2___ tens _____ ones

_____ tens _____ ones

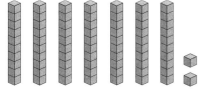

_____ tens _____ ones

Addition and Subtraction

Add or subtract. Watch the signs!

6 + 3 = _____   2 + 7 = _____   7 + 2 = _____

9 – 7 = _____   1 + 6 = _____   7 – 2 = _____

8 – 3 = _____   4 – 3 = _____   9 + 1 = _____

4 + 3 = _____   7 + 3 = _____   3 + 7 = _____

5 + 4 = _____   9 – 4 = _____   8 – 6 = _____

Count the wheels on the bikes by 2s.

Count the sandals by 2s.

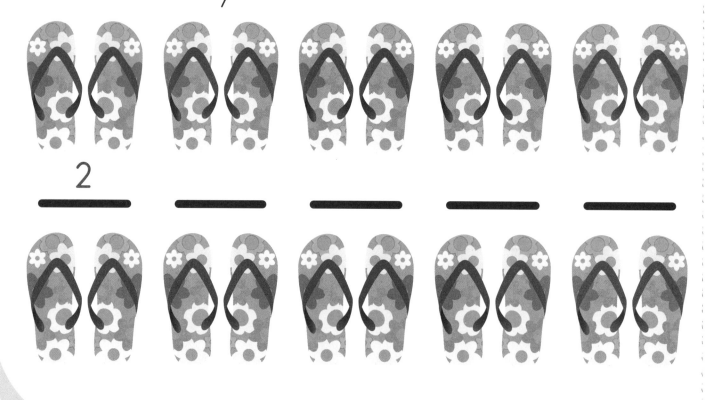

2

Each penny is worth 1 cent (¢). Count each row of pennies. Print the total number of cents on the line.

 __4__ ¢

 _____ ¢

_____ ¢

_____ ¢

Place Value

How many tens and how many ones make up each number? One is done for you.

12 = ___1___ tens and ___2___ ones

24 = _____ tens and _____ ones

51 = _____ tens and _____ ones

37 = _____ tens and _____ ones

42 = _____ tens and _____ ones

70 = _____ tens and _____ ones

19 = _____ tens and _____ ones

91 = _____ tens and _____ ones

1 = _____ tens and _____ ones

100 = _____ tens and _____ ones

Add or subtract with doubles. Watch the signs.

0	1	2	3	4	5	6
+0	+1	+2	+3	+4	+5	+6
(0)	◯	◯	◯	◯	◯	◯

0	1	2	3	4	5	6
−0	−1	−2	−3	−4	−5	−6
◯	◯	◯	◯	◯	◯	◯

Counting by 5s

Count the fingers by 5s.

5   __   __   __   __

__   __   __   __

Count out loud.

5, 10, 15, 20, 25, 30, 35, 40, 45,

50, 55, 60, 65, 70, 75, 80, 85,

90, 95, 100

Each nickel is worth 5 cents (¢).
Count each row of nickels. Print the total number of cents
on the line.

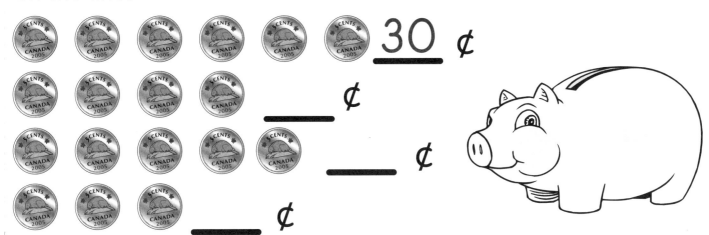

<u>30</u> ¢

_____ ¢

_____ ¢

_____ ¢

Sequencing Numbers

Write the number that comes after.

24, <u>25</u>   42, _____   63, _____   34, _____

Write the number that comes before.

<u>95,</u> 96   _____ , 48   _____ , 35   _____ , 50

Write the number that comes in between.

16, <u>17</u>, 18   62, _____ , 64   59, _____ , 61

Write the numbers that come before and after.

<u>16,</u> 17, <u>18</u>   _____ , 42, _____   _____ , 65, _____

How much is in each piggy bank?

6 ¢

___ ¢

___ ¢

___ ¢

___ ¢

___ ¢

Adding Three Numbers

Add. The first one has a hint to help you.

$$\begin{array}{r} 2 \\ 4 \\ +5 \\ \hline 11 \end{array}$$

$$\begin{array}{r} 3 \\ 1 \\ +7 \\ \hline \end{array}$$

$$\begin{array}{r} 1 \\ 8 \\ +4 \\ \hline \end{array}$$

$$\begin{array}{r} 4 \\ 5 \\ +3 \\ \hline \end{array}$$

$$\begin{array}{r} 4 \\ 3 \\ +3 \\ \hline \end{array}$$

$$\begin{array}{r} 5 \\ 2 \\ +3 \\ \hline \end{array}$$

Each dime is worth 10 cents (¢). Count each row of dimes.
Print the total number of cents on the line.

      60¢

    ___ ¢

      ___ ¢

    ___ ¢

Counting by 2s, 5s, 10s

Count out loud. Write the missing numbers.

2, 4, 6, ___, 10, ___, ___, 16, ___, 20, ___, 24, ___

28, ___, ___, 34, ___, ___, ___, 42, ___, ___, ___, 50

5, 10, 15, ___, ___, 30, ___, ___, ___, 50, ___, ___,

65, ___, ___, 80, ___, ___, ___, 100

10, ___, 30, ___, ___, 60, ___, ___, ___, 100

Count the change in each wallet.

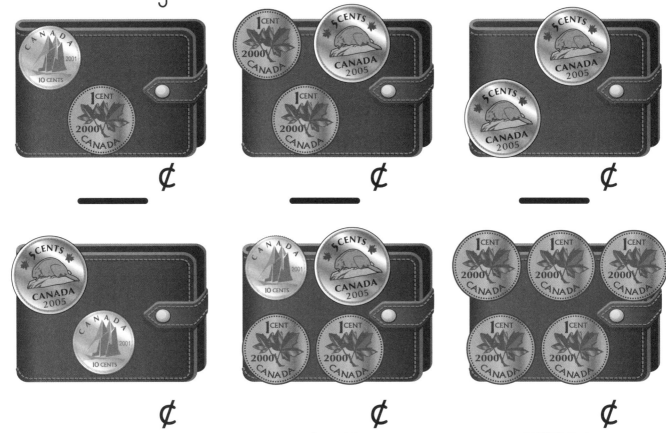

_____ ¢   _____ ¢   _____ ¢

_____ ¢   _____ ¢   _____ ¢

Place Value

Colour the box that shows the matching number.

Example:

3 tens 2 ones	**32**	
	12	

5 tens 3 ones	36
	53

6 tens 4 ones	64
	28

7 tens 1 ones	71
	17

4 tens 7 ones	41
	47

3 tens 0 ones	30
	10

Point to each number as you count backwards.

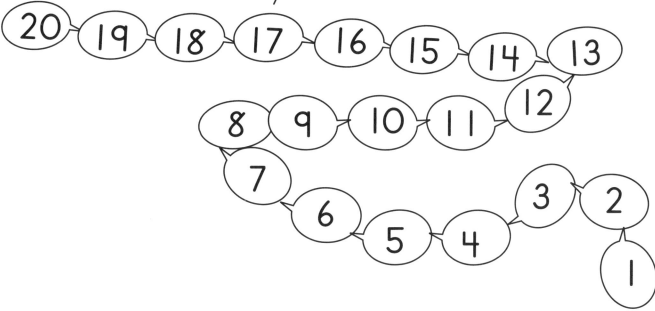

Coins

Count the money. Print the total on the line.

A loonie is $1.00

A toonie is $2.00

$ _____

$ _____

Put the **+** or **−** in the box to make the number sentence true.

6 □− 4 = 2   8 □− 5 = 3   3 □+ 5 = 8

7 □+ 4 = 11   5 □+ 4 = 9   4 □+ 4 = 8

9 □− 1 = 8   10 □− 6 = 4   5 □+ 6 = 11

9 □− 7 = 2   8 □− 3 = 5   12 □− 6 = 6

9 □+ 3 = 12   10 □− 7 = 3   4 □− 4 = 0

Add or subtract.

10 − 4 = __6__   3 + 7 = ___   5 + 6 = ___

9 − 4 = ___   6 + 2 = ___   7 + 3 = ___

4 + 5 = ___   4 − 3 = ___   10 − 3 = ___

9 − 7 = ___   4 − 2 = ___   6 + 4 = ___

8 − 3 = ___   9 − 6 = ___   8 + 2 = ___

Money

Count the money. Print the amount on the line.
Draw a line to the toy you can buy.

11¢

__15¢__

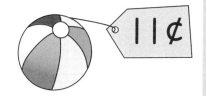
15¢

_____

12¢

_____

_____

20¢

Print the number beside the word.

one ___1___   five _____   three _____

seven _____   zero _____   nine _____

two _____   six _____   four _____

eight _____   ten _____

fourteen _____   sixteen _____   twelve _____

eighteen _____   eleven _____   thirteen _____

twenty _____   fifteen _____   nineteen _____

twenty-three ___ thirty ___   seventeen _____

Solving Word Problems

Arvid spent 7¢. Lia spent 3¢.

How much did they spend all together?   _____

Mina has 10 gumballs. Anna has 4 gumballs.
How many gumballs do they have all together?   _____

Circle the coins you need to buy each toy.

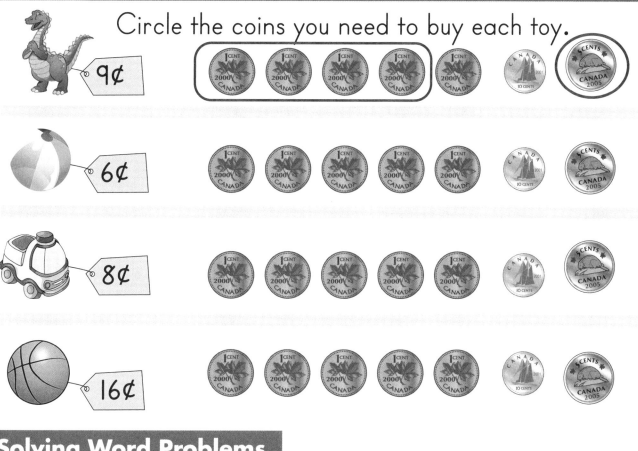

Solving Word Problems

Tim has 3 pencils. Ameya has 6 pencils.
How many pencils do they have all together? _____

Mia has 4 balloons. Kate has 7 balloons.
How many balloons do they have all together? _____

Count the wheels by 2s.

$\underline{\quad 2 \quad}$ $\underline{\qquad}$ $\underline{\qquad}$ $\underline{\qquad}$ $\underline{\qquad}$

Count the toes by 5s.

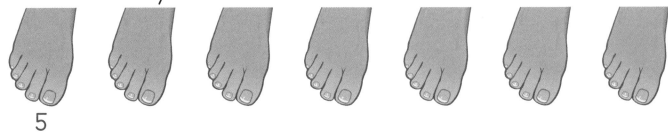

$\underline{\quad 5 \quad}$ $\underline{\qquad}$ $\underline{\qquad}$ $\underline{\qquad}$ $\underline{\qquad}$

Count the fingers by 10s.

$\underline{\qquad}$ $\underline{\qquad}$ $\underline{\qquad}$ $\underline{\qquad}$ $\underline{\qquad}$

Solving Word Problems

One has 4 balloons and the other has 6 balloons.
How many balloons all together?

One has 6 trains and the other has 3 trains.
How many trains all together?

$\underline{\qquad}$

$\underline{\qquad}$

Jack took these clothes out of his closet.

How many different ways can Jack get dressed? _____
Colour the pictures to show each way.

Add or subtract.

Match the answer to the colour in the key.

Colour the picture.

Key

7 = 5 = 6 =
8 = 9 = 4 =

9 – 4 = ___

4 + 4 = ___

$\begin{array}{r} 7 \\ +2 \\ \hline \end{array}$

12 – 5 = ___

$\begin{array}{r} 3 \\ +1 \\ \hline \end{array}$

$\begin{array}{r} 4 \\ +2 \\ \hline \end{array}$

9 – 4 = ___

12 – 5 = ___

Add or subtract.

Match the answer to the colour in the key.

Colour the picture.

Key

2 =

9 =

6 =

10 =

3+6 = ___

5+5= ___

8–6= ___

12–6 = ___

11–5 = ___

33

Ordinal numbers tell what order things are in.

first	second	third	fourth	fifth	sixth	seventh	eighth	ninth	tenth
1st	2nd	3rd	4th	5th	6th	7th	8th	9th	10th

Colour the fourth hat red. Colour the sixth hat green.

Colour the first hat blue. Colour the tenth hat green.

Colour the eighth mitt yellow. Colour the second mitt orange.

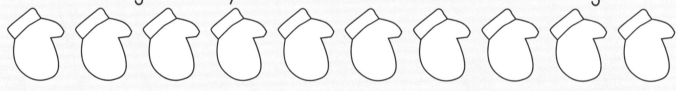

Colour the seventh mitt yellow. Colour the fifth mitt purple.

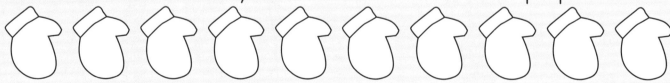

There are 8 toys in the toy box. Some belong to Max and some belong to Dax. Max has 2 more toys in the box than Dax.

How many toys does Max have in the box? _____

Addition and Subtraction

Add or subtract. Watch the signs!

8 +4	9 +6	7 −3	4 +5	6 +4	6 −3
◯	◯	◯	◯	◯	◯

8 −3	12 +6	19 −7	17 −3	7 +4	8 −4
◯	◯	◯	◯	◯	◯

Add or subtract.

$$\begin{array}{r} 7 \\ +4 \\ \hline \end{array}$$

$$\begin{array}{r} 8 \\ +6 \\ \hline \end{array}$$

$$\begin{array}{r} 9 \\ -3 \\ \hline \end{array}$$

$$\begin{array}{r} 6 \\ +5 \\ \hline \end{array}$$

$11-2 = $ _____

$14-6 = $ _____

$13-5 = $ _____

$17-1 = $ _____

Money

How many of each coin are in the piggy bank?
Write it on the line.

_____ pennies

_____ nickels

_____ dimes

_____ quarters

_____ loonies

_____ toonies

Count and add.

Matt has   and Gino has

_____6_____ + _____ = _____ ¢ in all

Shara has and Nada has

_____ + _____ = _____ ¢ in all

Lise has   and Fran has

_____ + _____ = _____ ¢ in all

Jamal has and Alex has

_____ + _____ = _____ ¢ in all

Addition and Subtraction

Put **+** or **−** on the line to make the number sentences true.

$8 \underline{+} 2 = 10$ $12 \underline{} 4 = 8$

$9 \underline{} 3 = 6$ $7 \underline{} 8 = 15$

$13 \underline{} 5 = 8$ $15 \underline{} 6 = 9$

$2 \underline{} 9 = 11$ $14 \underline{} 7 = 7$

Solve the word problems.
(Hint: Cross out some coins and count to find the answers.)

Tina has 13¢. She lends 9¢ to her sister.
How much does she have left?

_____ ¢ is left.

Amy has 17¢. She lends 15¢ to her brother.
How much does she have left?

_____ ¢ is left.

Dillon has 15¢. He spends 6¢ on a gumball.
How much does he have left?

_____ ¢ is left.

This pizza has two equal parts. Each part is $\frac{1}{2}$ of the whole.

Write $\frac{1}{2}$ on both parts of each shape.

Then colour $\frac{1}{2}$ of each shape red.

Colour the other $\frac{1}{2}$ blue.

Example:

$\frac{1}{2}$

$\frac{1}{2}$

This pizza has three equal parts.
Each part is $\frac{1}{3}$ of the whole.

Write $\frac{1}{3}$ on each part of each shape.
Then colour $\frac{1}{3}$ of each shape red,
$\frac{1}{3}$ blue, and $\frac{1}{3}$ yellow.

This pizza has four equal parts.
Each part is $\frac{1}{4}$ of the whole.

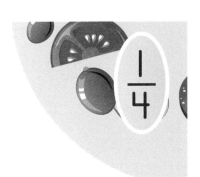

Write $\frac{1}{4}$ on each part of each shape.
Then colour $\frac{1}{4}$ of each shape red, $\frac{1}{4}$ blue,
$\frac{1}{4}$ yellow, and $\frac{1}{4}$ green.

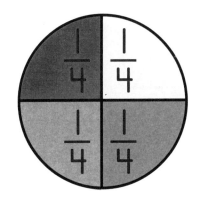

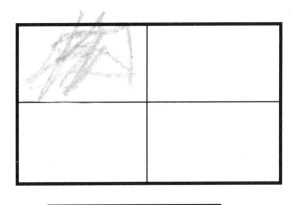

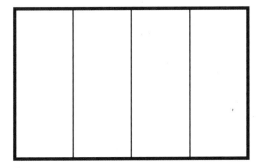

41

Colour only the shapes that show halves.
Put an X on the pictures that do NOT show halves.

Example:

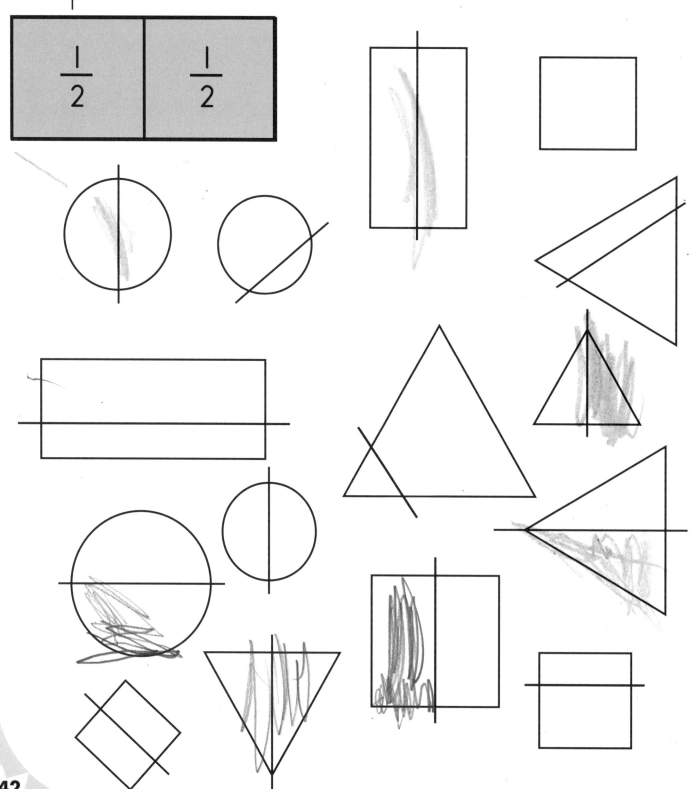

Use a paperclip ⬭ to measure things.

june 3

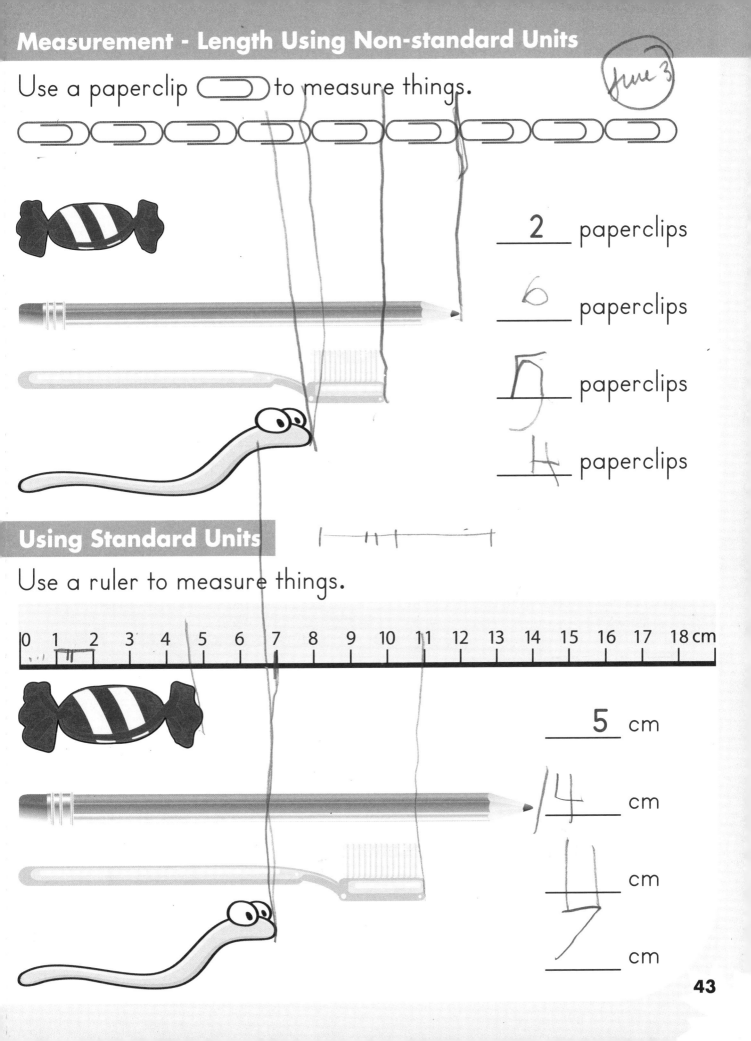

_2_ paperclips

_6_ paperclips

_5_ paperclips

_4_ paperclips

Use a ruler to measure things.

| 0 | 1 | 2 | 3 | 4 | 5 | 6 | 7 | 8 | 9 | 10 | 11 | 12 | 13 | 14 | 15 | 16 | 17 | 18 cm |

_5_ cm

_14_ cm

_4_ cm

___ cm

43

Colour the minute hand (long) red.
Colour the hour hand (short) green.
Print the numbers on the clock.

1 2 3 4 5 6 7 8 9 10 11 (12)

The short hand points to 3.

The long hand points to 12.
It is 3 o'clock or 3:00.

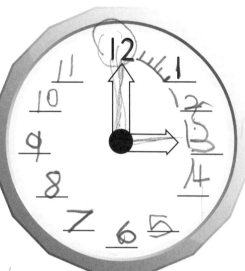

This number tells the hour. It is 3:00.

This number tells the minutes after the hour.

Telling Time to the Hour

What time does each clock say? Write the time on the line.
(Hint: The minute hand is long and hour hand is short.)

____:____

____:____

7:00

____:____

11:00

Colour the minute hand (long) red.
Colour the hour hand (short) green.

June 3

The short hour hand points past 3.
It is "something" past 3.

Skip count by 5s to count the minutes past the hour.

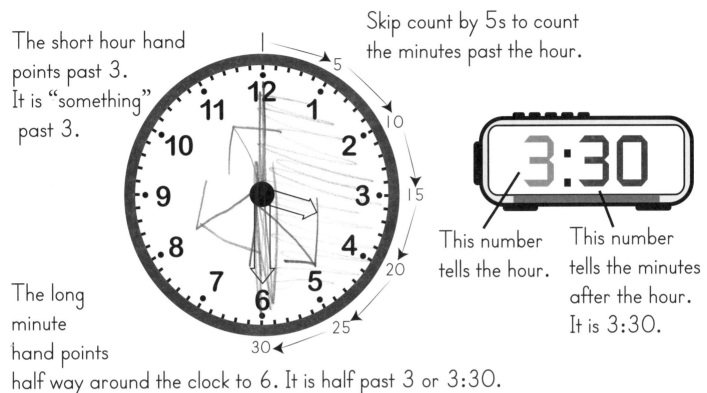

This number tells the hour.

This number tells the minutes after the hour.
It is 3:30.

The long minute hand points half way around the clock to 6. It is half past 3 or 3:30.

Telling Time to the Half Hour

What time does each clock say? Write the time on the line.

1:30

7:30

12:30

10:30

4:30

Draw a line to connect the clocks that tell the same time.

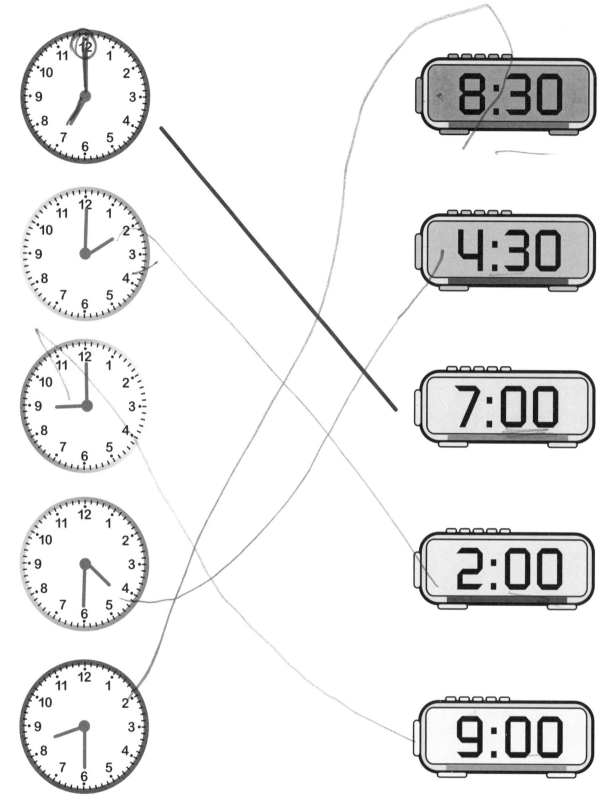

June 3

Circle the biggest.

Circle the tallest.

Circle the longest.

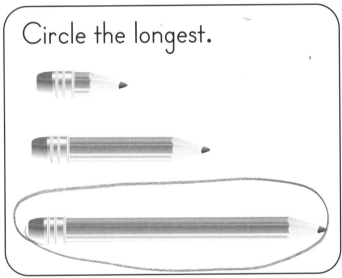

Circle the widest.

Circle the thinnest.

Circle the heaviest.

Circle the container that holds more.

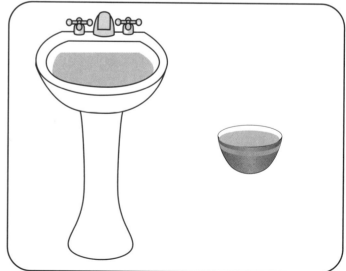

Measurement – Capacity

Look at the first container in each row.
Circle another container that holds about the same amount.

Months have 30 or 31 days, except February, which has 28 or 29 days.

July

Sunday	Monday	Tuesday	Wednesday	Thursday	Friday	Saturday
	1 🍁	2	3	4	5	6
7	8	9	10	11	12	13
14	15	16	17	18	19	20
21	22	23	24	25	26	27
28	29	30	31			

Use the calendar above to answer the questions.

1. Canada's birthday is on July 1st.
   What day of the week is Canada Day on?_____

2. How many Mondays are in July?_____

3. Mary has a play date on July 19th. Today is July 16th.
   How many days until her play date ?_____

4. What month comes after July?_____

Geometry and Spatial Sense

Trace the picture. Then copy it.

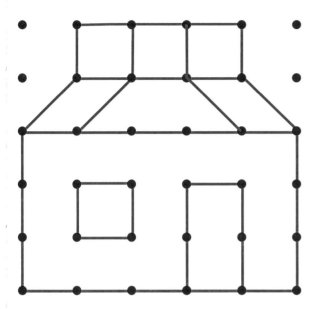 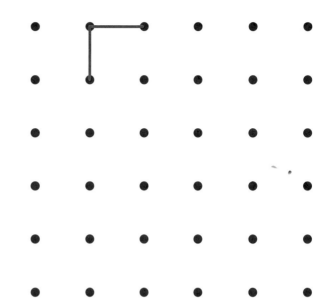

Identifying Shapes and Shape Words

Colour each shape. Draw a line from each shape to the matching word. Then copy the word on the line.

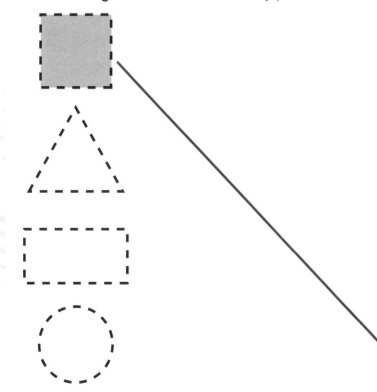

triangle _____

rectangle _____

circle _____

square _____

How many shapes can you find?

circle   rectangle   triangle   square

Shape	How many?
○	
▭	
△	
□	

Symmetry

Draw a line to divide each snack into 2 equal halves.

Geometry and Spatial Sense - 3-D Shapes

Draw a line from each object to the matching shape.

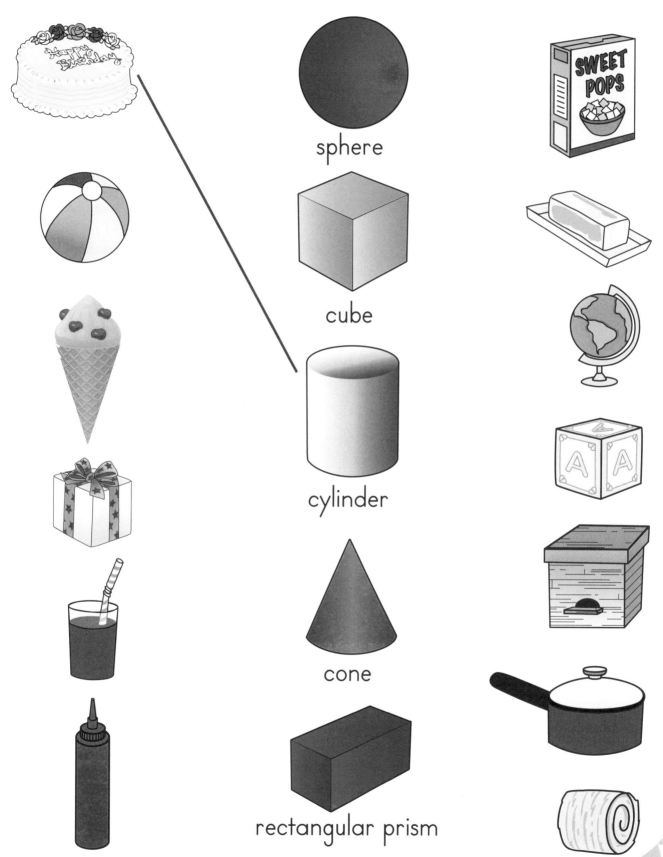

sphere

cube

cylinder

cone

rectangular prism

Draw the shapes that continues each pattern.

ABCABCABC____ __ __ __

Identify the Core

These three items repeat to create a pattern. They are called the **core**.

Circle the **core** of each pattern.

Look at the picture graph. Answer the questions.

Favourite Snacks in Ms. Bertin's Class

Fruit	🍎	🍎	🍎	
Granola Bars				
Vegetables				
Cheese and Crackers				

Each snack represents 1 child.

How many children like fruit best? _____

How many children like granola bars best? _____

How many children like vegetables best? _____

How many children like cheese and crackers best? _____

More children like granola bars best than like cheese and crackers best. How many more? _____
(Hint: Use subtraction.)

How many children in all voted for their favourite snack?

_____

Decide whether each picture is **likely** or **unlikely**.
Circle the word you chose.

likely   unlikely

likely   unlikely

likely   unlikely

likely   unlikely

Sequencing

Number the pictures to show the correct order.

Solutions

Page 2

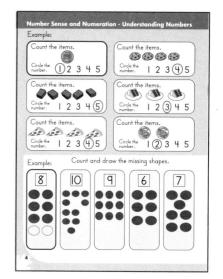

Page 3

Number Sense and Numeration - Understanding Numbers

Page 4

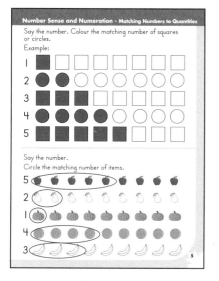

Page 5

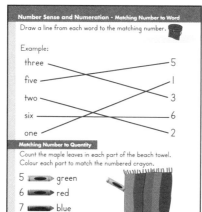

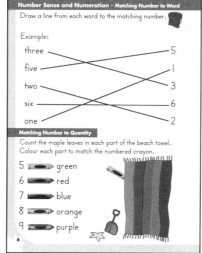

Page 6

Number Sense and Numeration - Number Words

Count the maple leaves. Fill in the blanks.

t e n

s i x

t h r e e

f i v e

o n e

e i g h t

z e r o

n i n e

t w o

s e v e n

| 0 = zero |
| 1 = one |
| 2 = two |
| 3 = three |
| 4 = four |
| 5 = five |
| 6 = six |
| 7 = seven |
| 8 = eight |
| 9 = nine |
| 10 = ten |

Page 7

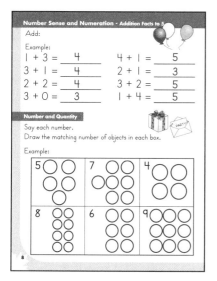

Page 8

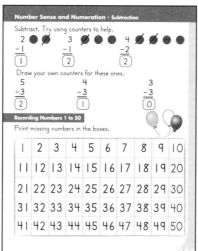

Page 9

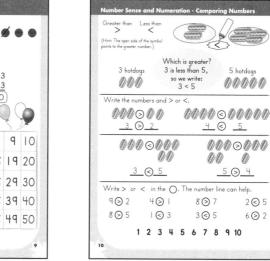

Page 10

57

Solutions

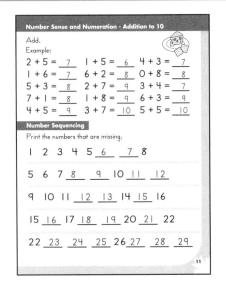

Number Sense and Numeration · Addition to 10

Add.
Example:
2 + 5 = 7   1 + 5 = 6   4 + 3 = 7
1 + 6 = 7   6 + 2 = 8   0 + 8 = 8
5 + 3 = 8   2 + 7 = 9   3 + 4 = 7
7 + 1 = 8   1 + 8 = 9   6 + 3 = 9
4 + 5 = 9   3 + 7 = 10 5 + 5 = 10

Number Sequencing

Print the numbers that are missing.

1 2 3 4 5 6 7 8
5 6 7 8 9 10 11 12
9 10 11 12 13 14 15 16
15 16 17 18 19 20 21 22
22 23 24 25 26 27 28 29

Page 11

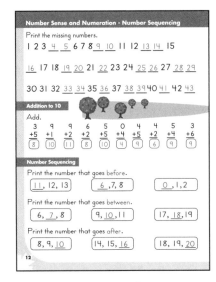

Number Sense and Numeration · Number Sequencing

Print the missing numbers.
1 2 3 4 5 6 7 8 9 10 11 12 13 14 15
16 17 18 19 20 21 22 23 24 25 26 27 28 29
30 31 32 33 34 35 36 37 38 39 40 41 42 43

Addition to 10

Add.
3+5=8 9+1=10 9+2=11 6+2=8 5+5=10 0+4=4 4+5=9 4+2=6 5+4=9 3+6=9

Number Sequencing

Print the number that goes before.
11, 12, 13   6, 7, 8   0, 1, 2

Print the number that goes between.
6, 7, 8   9, 10, 11   17, 18, 19

Print the number that goes after.
8, 9, 10   14, 15, 16   18, 19, 20

Page 12

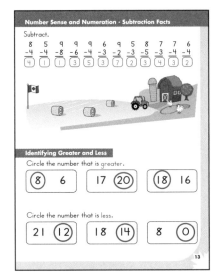

Number Sense and Numeration · Subtraction Facts

Subtract.
8-4=4 5-4=1 9-8=1 9-6=3 6-4=5 9-3=... 5-2=... 8-3=5 7-4=... 7-4=... 6-4=2

Identifying Greater and Less

Circle the number that is greater.
(8) 6   17 (20)   (18) 16

Circle the number that is less.
21 (12)   18 (14)   8 (0)

Page 13

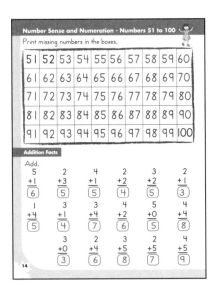

Number Sense and Numeration · Numbers 51 to 100

Print missing numbers in the boxes.

51	52	53	54	55	56	57	58	59	60
61	62	63	64	65	66	67	68	69	70
71	72	73	74	75	76	77	78	79	80
81	82	83	84	85	86	87	88	89	90
91	92	93	94	95	96	97	98	99	100

Addition Facts

Add.
5+1=6 2+3=5 4+1=5 2+2=4 3+2=5 2+1=3
1+4=5 3+1=4 3+4=7 4+2=6 5+0=5 4+4=8
3+0=3 2+4=6 3+5=8 2+5=7 4+5=9

Page 14

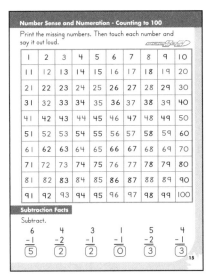

Number Sense and Numeration · Counting to 100

Print the missing numbers. Then touch each number and say it out loud.

1	2	3	4	5	6	7	8	9	10
11	12	13	14	15	16	17	18	19	20
21	22	23	24	25	26	27	28	29	30
31	32	33	34	35	36	37	38	39	40
41	42	43	44	45	46	47	48	49	50
51	52	53	54	55	56	57	58	59	60
61	62	63	64	65	66	67	68	69	70
71	72	73	74	75	76	77	78	79	80
81	82	83	84	85	86	87	88	89	90
91	92	93	94	95	96	97	98	99	100

Subtraction Facts

Subtract.
6-1=5 3-2=... 3-1=2 1-1=0 5-2=3 4-1=3

Page 15

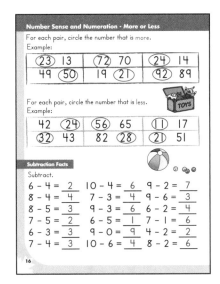

Number Sense and Numeration · More or Less

For each pair, circle the number that is more.
Example:
(23) 13   (72) 70   (24) 14
49 (50)   19 (21)   (92) 89

For each pair, circle the number that is less.
Example:
42 (24)   (56) 65   (11) 17
(32) 43   82 (28)   (21) 51

Subtraction Facts

Subtract.
6 - 4 = 2   10 - 4 = 6   9 - 2 = 7
8 - 4 = 4   7 - 3 = 4   9 - 6 = 3
8 - 5 = 3   9 - 3 = 6   6 - 2 = 4
7 - 5 = 2   6 - 5 = 1   7 - 1 = 6
6 - 3 = 3   9 - 0 = 9   4 - 2 = 2
7 - 4 = 3   10 - 6 = 4   8 - 2 = 6

Page 16

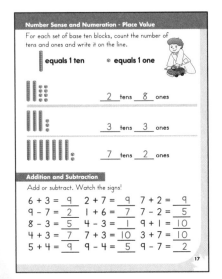

Number Sense and Numeration · Place Value

For each set of base ten blocks, count the number of tens and ones and write it on the line.

▮ equals 1 ten   ● equals 1 one

2 tens 8 ones
3 tens 3 ones
7 tens 2 ones

Addition and Subtraction

Add or subtract. Watch the signs!
6 + 3 = 9   2 + 7 = 9   7 + 2 = 9
9 - 7 = 2   1 + 6 = 7   7 - 2 = 5
8 - 3 = 5   4 - 3 = 1   9 + 1 = 10
4 + 3 = 7   7 + 3 = 10   3 + 7 = 10
5 + 4 = 9   9 - 4 = 5   9 - 7 = 2

Page 17

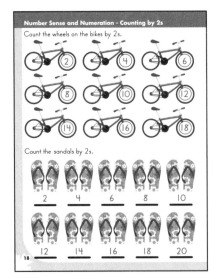

Number Sense and Numeration · Counting by 2s

Count the wheels on the bikes by 2s.
2 4 6 8 10 12 14 16 18

Count the sandals by 2s.
2 4 6 8 10
12 14 16 18 20

Page 18

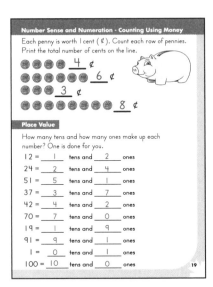

Number Sense and Numeration · Counting Using Money

Each penny is worth 1 cent (¢). Count each row of pennies. Print the total number of cents on the line.
4 ¢
6 ¢
3 ¢
8 ¢

Place Value

How many tens and how many ones make up each number? One is done for you.
12 = 1 tens and 2 ones
24 = 2 tens and 4 ones
51 = 5 tens and 1 ones
37 = 3 tens and 7 ones
42 = 4 tens and 2 ones
70 = 7 tens and 0 ones
19 = 1 tens and 9 ones
91 = 9 tens and 1 ones
1 = 0 tens and 1 ones
100 = 10 tens and 0 ones

Page 19

Solutions

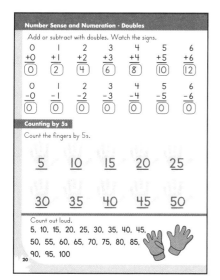

Page 20

Number Sense and Numeration - Doubles

Add or subtract with doubles. Watch the signs.

0	1	2	3	4	5	6
+0	+1	+2	+3	+4	+5	+6
0	2	4	6	8	10	12

0	1	2	3	4	5	6
-0	-1	-2	-3	-4	-5	-6
0	0	0	0	0	0	0

Counting by 5s

Count the fingers by 5s.

5 10 15 20 25
30 35 40 45 50

Count out loud.

5, 10, 15, 20, 25, 30, 35, 40, 45,
50, 55, 60, 65, 70, 75, 80, 85,
90, 95, 100

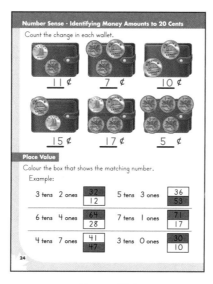

Page 21

Number Sense and Numeration - Counting Using Money

Each nickel is worth 5 cents (¢).
Count each row of nickels. Print the total number of cents on the line.

30 ¢
20 ¢
25 ¢
15 ¢

Sequencing Numbers

Write the number that comes after.

24, 25   42, 43   63, 64   34, 35

Write the number that comes before.

95, 96   47, 48   34, 35   49, 50

Write the number that comes in between.

16, 17, 18   62, 63, 64   59, 60, 61

Write the numbers that come before and after.

16, 17, 18   41, 42, 43   64, 65, 66

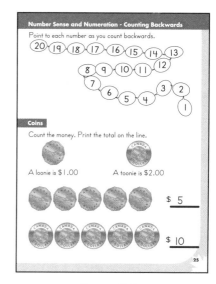

Page 22

Number Sense and Numeration - Counting Coins to 20 Cents

How much is in each piggy bank?

6 ¢   20 ¢
6 ¢   14 ¢
7 ¢   11 ¢

Adding Three Numbers

Add. The first one has a hint to help you.

2	3	1	4	4	5
4	1	8	5	3	2
+5	+7	+4	+3	+3	+3
11	11	13	12	10	10

Page 23

Number Sense and Numeration - Counting 10s Using Money

Each dime is worth 10 cents (¢). Count each row of dimes.
Print the total number of cents on the line.

60 ¢
40 ¢
50 ¢
30 ¢

Counting by 2s, 5s, 10s

Count out loud. Write the missing numbers.

2, 4, 6, 8, 10, 12, 14, 16, 18, 20, 22, 24, 26
28, 30, 32, 34, 36, 38, 40, 42, 44, 46, 48, 50

5, 10, 15, 20, 25, 30, 35, 40, 45, 50, 55, 60,
65, 70, 75, 80, 85, 90, 95, 100

10, 20, 30, 40, 50, 60, 70, 80, 90, 100

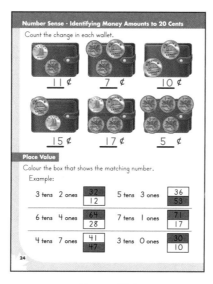

Page 24

Number Sense - Identifying Money Amounts to 20 Cents

Count the change in each wallet.

11 ¢   7 ¢   10 ¢
15 ¢   17 ¢   5 ¢

Place Value

Colour the box that shows the matching number.
Example:

3 tens 2 ones	32 / 12	5 tens 3 ones	36 / 53
6 tens 4 ones	64 / 28	7 tens 1 ones	71 / 17
4 tens 7 ones	41 / 47	3 tens 0 ones	30 / 10

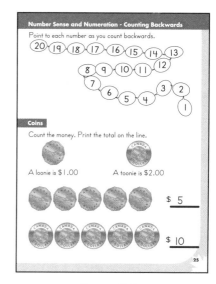

Page 25

Number Sense and Numeration - Counting Backwards

Point to each number as you count backwards.

20, 19, 18, 17, 16, 15, 14, 13, 12, 11, 10, 9, 8, 7, 6, 5, 4, 3, 2, 1

Coins

Count the money. Print the total on the line.

A loonie is $1.00   A toonie is $2.00

$ 5

$ 10

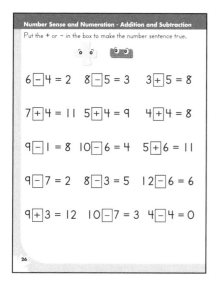

Page 26

Number Sense and Numeration - Addition and Subtraction

Put the + or – in the box to make the number sentence true.

6 – 4 = 2   8 – 5 = 3   3 + 5 = 8

7 + 4 = 11   5 + 4 = 9   4 + 4 = 8

9 – 1 = 8   10 – 6 = 4   5 + 6 = 11

9 – 7 = 2   8 – 3 = 5   12 – 6 = 6

9 + 3 = 12   10 – 7 = 3   4 – 4 = 0

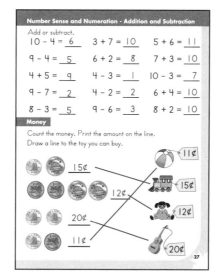

Page 27

Number Sense and Numeration - Addition and Subtraction

Add or subtract.

10 – 4 = 6   3 + 7 = 10   5 + 6 = 11
9 – 4 = 5   6 + 2 = 8   7 + 3 = 10
4 + 5 = 9   4 – 3 = 1   10 – 3 = 7
9 – 7 = 2   4 – 2 = 2   6 + 4 = 10
8 – 3 = 5   9 – 6 = 3   8 + 2 = 10

Money

Count the money. Print the amount on the line.
Draw a line to the toy you can buy.

15¢ → 11¢
12¢ → 15¢
20¢ → 12¢
11¢ → 20¢

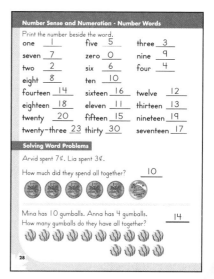

Page 28

Number Sense and Numeration - Number Words

Print the number beside the word.

one	1	five	5	three	3
seven	7	zero	0	nine	9
two	2	six	6	four	4
eight	8	ten	10		
fourteen	14	sixteen	16	twelve	12
eighteen	18	eleven	11	thirteen	13
twenty	20	fifteen	15	nineteen	19
twenty-three	23	thirty	30	seventeen	17

Solving Word Problems

Arvid spent 7¢. Lia spent 3¢.
How much did they spend all together?   10

Mina has 10 gumballs. Anna has 4 gumballs.
How many gumballs do they have all together?   14

Solutions

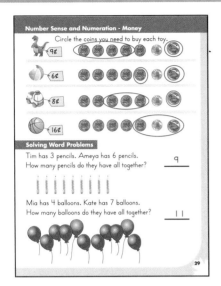

Page 29

Page 30

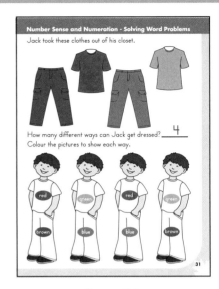

Page 31

Page 32

Page 33

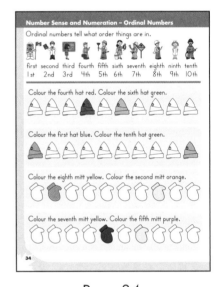

Page 34

Page 35

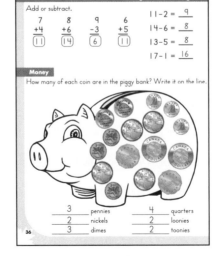

Page 36

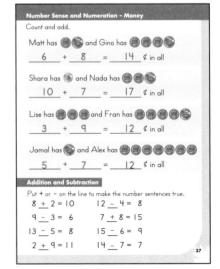

Page 37

Solutions

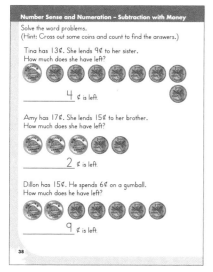

Number Sense and Numeration – Subtraction with Money

Solve the word problems.
(Hint: Cross out some coins and count to find the answers.)

Tina has 13¢. She lends 9¢ to her sister.
How much does she have left?

___4___ ¢ is left.

Amy has 17¢. She lends 15¢ to her brother.
How much does she have left?

___2___ ¢ is left.

Dillon has 15¢. He spends 6¢ on a gumball.
How much does he have left?

___9___ ¢ is left.

Page 38

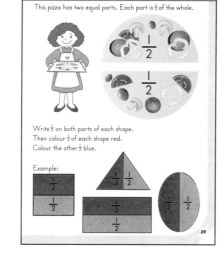

Number Sense and Numeration – Fractions – One Half

This pizza has two equal parts. Each part is ½ of the whole.

Write ½ on both parts of each shape.
Then colour ½ of each shape red.
Colour the other ½ blue.

Example:

Page 39

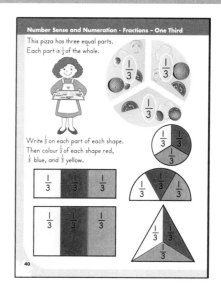

Number Sense and Numeration – Fractions – One Third

This pizza has three equal parts.
Each part is ⅓ of the whole.

Write ⅓ on each part of each shape.
Then colour ⅓ of each shape red,
⅓ blue, and ⅓ yellow.

Page 40

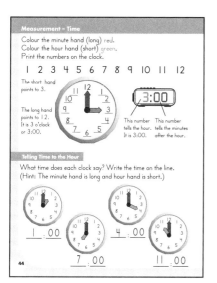

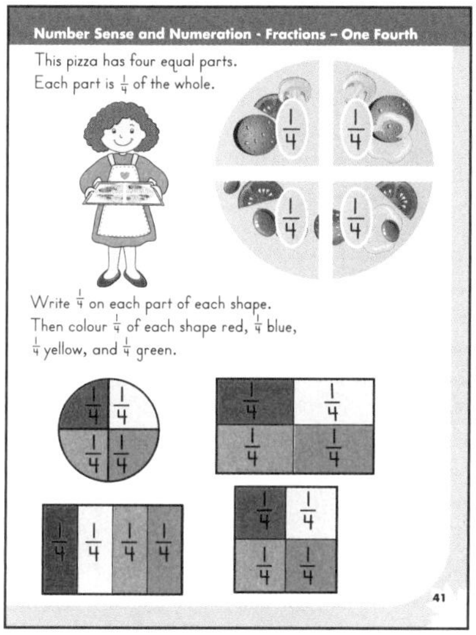

Number Sense and Numeration – Fractions – One Fourth

This pizza has four equal parts.
Each part is ¼ of the whole.

Write ¼ on each part of each shape.
Then colour ¼ of each shape red, ¼ blue,
¼ yellow, and ¼ green.

Page 41

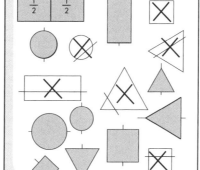

Number Sense and Numeration – Fractions – One Half

Colour only the shapes that show halves.
Put an X on the pictures that do NOT show halves.

Example:

Page 42

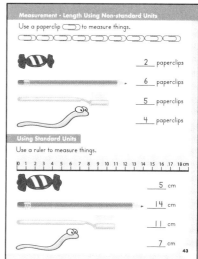

Measurement – Length Using Non-standard Units

Use a paperclip to measure things.

___2___ paperclips
___6___ paperclips
___5___ paperclips
___4___ paperclips

Using Standard Units

Use a ruler to measure things.

___5___ cm
___14___ cm
___11___ cm
___7___ cm

Page 43

Measurement – Time

Colour the minute hand (long) red.
Colour the hour hand (short) green.
Print the numbers on the clock.

1 2 3 4 5 6 7 8 9 10 11 12

The short hand points to 3.

The long hand points to 12.
It is 3 o'clock or 3:00.

3:00

This number tells the hour. It is 3:00.
This number tells the minutes after the hour.

Telling Time to the Hour

What time does each clock say? Write the time on the line.
(Hint: The minute hand is long and hour hand is short.)

___3___:00
___7___:00

___2___:00
___11___:00

Page 44

Measurement – Time

Colour the minute hand (long) red.
Colour the hour hand (short) green.

The short hour hand points past 3.
It is "something" past 3.

Skip count by 5s to count the minutes past the hour.

3:30

This number tells the hour.
This number tells the minutes after the hour. It is 3:30.

The long minute hand points half way around the clock to 6. It is half past 3 or 3:30.

Telling Time to the Half Hour

What time does each clock say? Write the time on the line.

1:30
7:30
12:30

10:30
4:30
6:30

Page 45

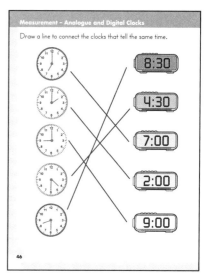

Measurement – Analogue and Digital Clocks

Draw a line to connect the clocks that tell the same time.

8:30
4:30
7:00
2:00
9:00

Page 46

61

Solutions

Page 47

Page 48

Page 49

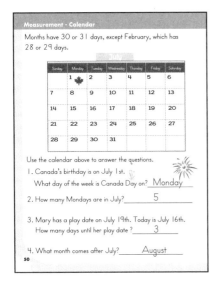

Page 50

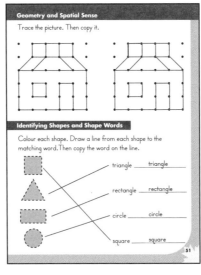

Page 51

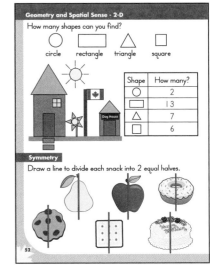

Page 52

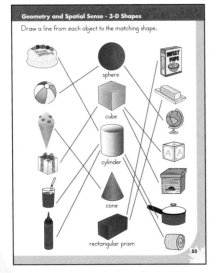

Page 53

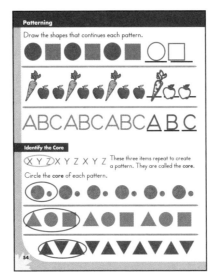

Page 54

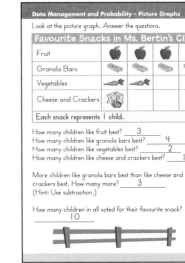

Page 55

Solutions

Page 56

Dot-to-dot Puzzle

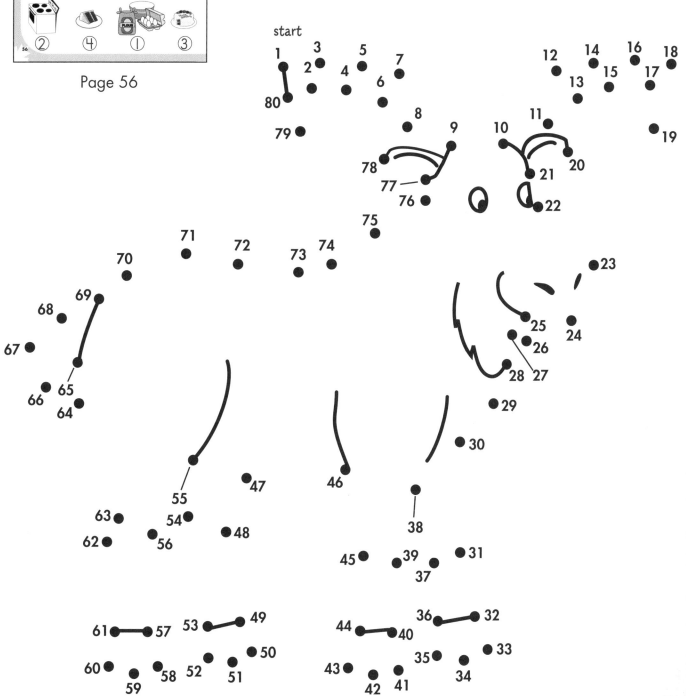

Written by teachers working in the Canadian classroom

Reading 1

- Letter sounds, sight words
- Vowel sounds, plurals
- Picture clues, rhyming
- Reading comprehension activities
- And much more!

D. J. Whitlock, B.Ed.

Grade 1 Reading

Contents

Initial Sounds

Initial sounds are what we hear at the beginning of words.
Say each letter. Say the sound each letter makes.
Circle the letter that make the initial sound for each picture.

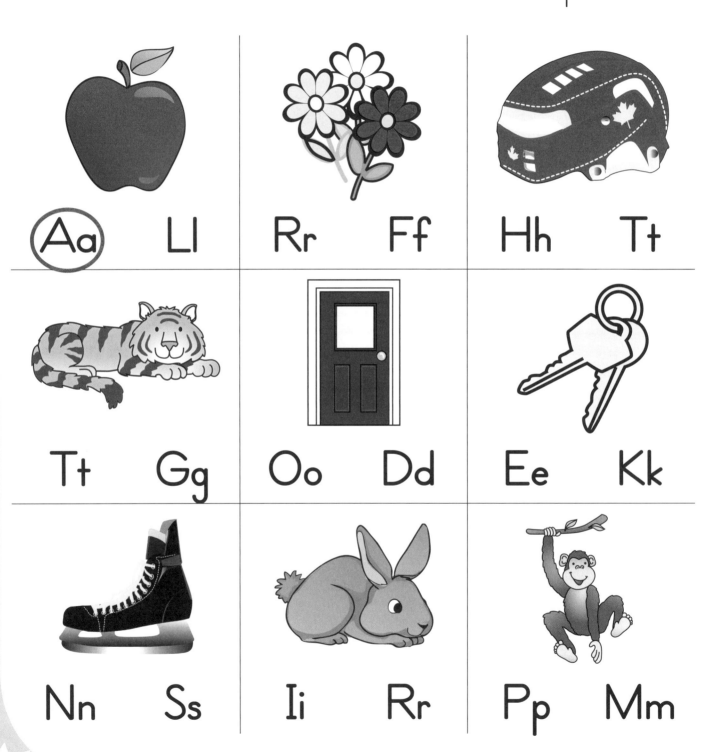

2

Initial Sounds

Look at each picture. Write the letter that makes the initial sound for each picture.

_c_ ar

___ ettle

___ uck

___ lag

___ alloons

___ mbrella

___ ruck

___ ouse

___ nake

Letters, Sounds, and Words

Final Sounds

Final sounds are what we hear at the end of words. Look at each picture. Write the letter that makes the final sound for each picture.

ice crea m

bal ___

hamburge ___

boo ___

carro ___

yo-y ___

be ___

octopu ___

trai ___

Scrambled Letters

Unscramble the word. Write the word on the line.

n a f

fan

i g p

_____

r c a

_____

g b u

_____

t a b

_____

p m a

_____

10

t n e

_____

a c t

_____

Plurals

Words that refer to more than one of something are plurals.
Look at the pictures. Write the plural words.
Use the Plural Word List if you need help.

Plural Word List

| dogs | balls | apples | crayons | trees | frogs |

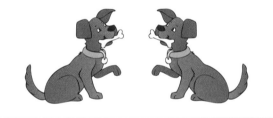

apples

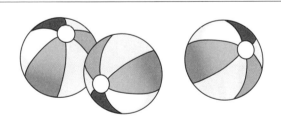

Picture Clues

Pictures help you!
Read the sentence. Circle the word that makes sense. Then, write the word.

Mom is at the __park__ .

(park)   plant

I ride in a _____ .

car   cat

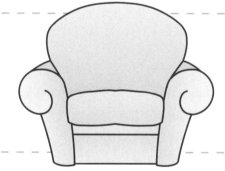

I sit on a _____ .

sofa   chair

I ride in a _____ .

bus   box

Dad has a _____ .

bike   boat

Sight Words

Learning sight words makes reading easier.
Practice these sight words with an adult.

the	or	by	up	no
is	of	that	but	like
in	and	was	not	my
it	a	are	can	what
to	you	with	said	were
I	see	they	an	when
he	for	this	she	come
at	on	saw	do	have
be	as	had	so	some
we	his	all	look	into

there				came
if				down
go				them
will				would
out				could
then				went
yes				her
make				am
little				get
here				want

Sight Words

Unscramble these sight words. Write them correctly. Use the Sight Word Bank to help.

Sight Word Bank

at
will
by
is
you
be
was
this
they
said
for
come

si	ouy	yeht
is		

eb	swa	yb

rof	liwl	meco

siht	ta	iads

9

Letters, Sounds, and Words

Sight Word Search

Find and circle the sight words in the puzzle.
Words are across or down.

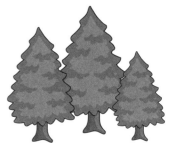

a	b	l	i	g	k	j	w	t	b	h	a	v	e	a
l	k	w	f	i	n	t	o	c	v	s	m	s	o	y
i	p	r	g	b	l	x	c	l	n	a	n	a	x	e
t	d	a	j	v	p	t	t	h	a	t	r	i	t	s
t	f	l	d	q	z	l	o	w	n	l	o	d	o	t
l	r	l	e	d	e	n	s	q	d	v	p	s	o	v
e	t	v	w	t	h	e	a	z	r	e	w	h	e	n
y	l	o	o	k	e	m	l	i	k	e	r	j	n	i

Find these words:

look	like	little	all	said	have
that	when	and	into	the	yes

10

Picture Clues and Sight Words

Practice Reading with Picture Clues and Sight Words

Use the pictures to help you read the sentences.
The sight words have been underlined.
Sound out the words. Practice reading each sentence.

The boy is in the wagon.

The frog is on the log.

The sheep was at the barn.

He has a green hat and red shoes.

Picture Clues and Sight Words

Picture Match

Match each sentence to the picture.
Underline the sight words in the sentence.

<u>The</u> girl <u>is</u> <u>in</u> <u>the</u> bathtub.

The girl is on the beach.

The girl is at school.

The girl is riding her bike.

The girl is in the kitchen.

The girl is at a party.

More Picture Clues

Can You Find the Match?

Match each picture to the words that make sense.
The first one is done for you.

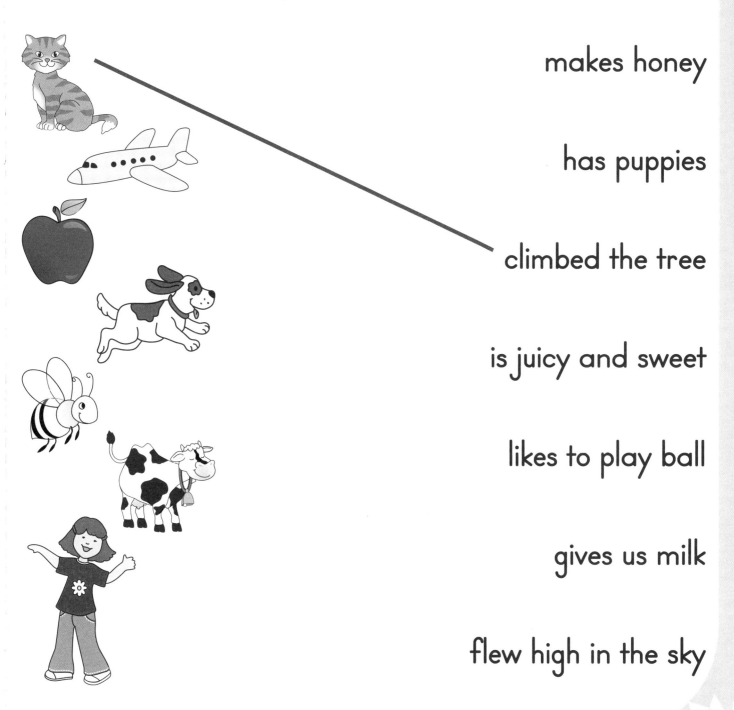

makes honey

has puppies

climbed the tree

is juicy and sweet

likes to play ball

gives us milk

flew high in the sky

Colour Clues

Read each sentence. Find the word in the Word Bank that makes sense. Print the word on the line.

> ## Word Bank
>
> yellow   black   red   green   blue   purple   orange   white

He wore _____ jeans to school.

The stop sign was bright _____.

Spring leaves on the tree are _____.

Nice puffy _____ clouds are in the sky.

The boy put _____ mustard on his hotdog.

The sky was _____ at night.

She put _____ grape jelly on her bread.

At Halloween the _____ pumpkin was ready to cut.

Rhyming

Rhyming Words

Read each sentence. Do you hear the two rhyming words? Underline the words that rhyme.

The <u>hat</u> was on the <u>cat</u>.

I can bake a cake.

She ate a bun in the sun.

There is a bug on the rug.

The pig is wearing a wig.

The frog jumped on a log.

Rhyming

More Rhyming Words

Fill in the blanks with words that rhyme with the underlined word. Use the pictures as clues.

The ___man___ drove a delivery <u>van</u>.

The boy hit his <u>head</u> _____ when he fell off the _____ .

After <u>school</u>, _____ I swam in the _____ .

With my _____ , I print the number <u>ten</u>.

I skinned my _____ climbing a <u>tree</u>.

Detail Words

Who or What?

Detail Words like "who" or "what" provide information. The circled words tell us "who" or "what." Print "who" or "what" on each line.

My dad is at home. <u>**who**</u>

Children love to eat candy. _____

The girl got new shoes. _____

The magician did neat tricks. _____

Farrah and her friend went to the park. _____

The car drove on the road. _____

The bird flew to the tree. _____

Detail Words

When or Where?

Detail Words like "when" or "where" provide information. The circled words tell us "when" or "where." Print "when" or "where" on each line.

On (Halloween,) I get candy. **when**

The milk is (in the fridge.) _____

(Tomorrow,) we go to school. _____

The pig rolled (in the mud.) _____

The hat is (on his head.) _____

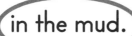

In (December,) it will snow. _____

On (Monday,) I go swimming. _____

18

Nouns - People

Community Helpers

Community helpers are people who do jobs that help others. Draw a line to connect each sentence with the correct community helper.

I help students read and do math.

I put out fires.

I deliver mail.

I tend to people when they are sick.

I keep people safe.

I take care of animals.

I look at your teeth.

Nouns - Objects

Pick an Object

Read the sentences. Look at the pictures. Print the sentence number in the box to show which object goes with each sentence.

1. Print your name with this.
2. Eat ice cream with this.
3. Cut paper with this.
4. Boil water in this.

5. Watch your favourite show on this.
6. Make your hair neat with this.
7. Cut an apple with this.
8. Put in a nail with this.

Closed Questions

Yes or No

Questions that can be answered with
yes or no are closed questions.
Read each question. Is the answer yes or no?
Circle your answer.

Can a bird fly? (yes) no

Is an apple a vegetable?   yes   no

Is a puppy a baby dog? yes   no

Is it cold in the winter?   yes   no

Will it snow in the summer?   yes   no

Is chocolate a healthy snack?   yes   no

Can a lion eat a mouse?   yes   no

Is grass orange?   yes   no

Do fish swim in water?   yes   no

Do cars drive on the road?   yes   no

Sentences

Choose the Best Sentence

Read each sentence. Select the sentence that best describes the picture. Underline the sentence.

The toys are a mess.

Dad put the toys away.

<u>The teddy bear, clown, and car are in the toy box.</u>

The girl is going to school.

The girl loves the bath.

The girl is going to bed.

The boy is going swimming.

The boy is playing in the sand.

The boy has a ball.

Sentences

Picture Match

Look at each picture. Read each sentence.
Match each sentence with the best picture.

This keeps you warm.

This protects you from the sun.

This is a sport cap.

These have Velcro.

These have laces.

These are blue.

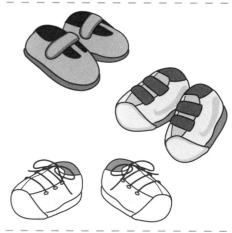

This ball is for kicking.

This ball is for hitting with a bat.

This ball is for playing in a pool.

Sentences

Choose the Best Sentence

Look at each picture. Read each sentence. Draw a line from the picture to the sentence that best describes the picture.

The loon is flying.

The loon swims in the lake.

The loon is on the shore.

The bike has 2 wheels.

The bike goes fast.

The girl is on the bike.

Ice cream is a cool treat.

The cake is chocolate.

The dog is barking.

It is breakfast time.

The pancakes have syrup on them.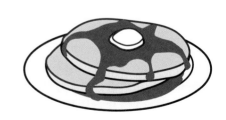

I am hungry.

Sentences

Choose the Best Sentence

Look at each picture. Read each sentence. Draw a line from the picture to the sentence that best describes the picture.

Fruit is healthy.

Cupcakes are good.

I had chicken for lunch.

An octopus has eight legs.

Fish swim in water.

Octopus eat fish.

Strawberries grow in trees.

I had ice cream for dessert.

Strawberries are a fruit.

The giraffe swims.

Two giraffes sleep.

The giraffe has a long neck.

Paragraphs and Titles

Choose the Best Title

Read each paragraph. Read the three titles. Underline the title that best describes the paragraph.

Sarah put on her blue bathing suit. She walked to the pool. Then she jumped in the water and made a splash.

<u>Swimming</u>

Sarah Likes to Play

A Hot Day

A dog can run. Monkeys can run too. But a cheetah is the fastest runner of all!

Run

Animals That Run

Running Dogs

Spread out the dough. Add some sauce and cheese. Put the pizza in the oven. Enjoy!

Making a Pizza

Baking

Food

Mohamed puts his skates on. He grabs his stick and a puck. Then he goes on the ice and scores a goal.

Skating

Cold Winter

Mohamed Plays Hockey

Following Directions

Picture Perfect

Read the sentences. Draw a picture to explain the words.

The circle is smaller than
the square.

Two balloons are red.
One balloon is blue.

The yellow flower is in
the green grass.

The tree has red apples.

Following Directions

More Picture Perfect

Read the sentences. Follow the instructions.

Colour the house blue.
Draw 3 flowers beside the house.

Colour the shoe red.
Draw a soccer ball beside it.

Colour the duck yellow.
Draw a duckling beside it.

Colour the car green.
Draw a brown dog beside it.

Picture Clues

Reading with Picture Clues

Read the story. Use the pictures to help you.
Answer the questions.

Brad brushed his teeth.

He put his pyjamas on.

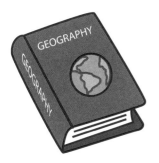

He read a book.

Brad kissed his mom.

He turned out the light.

 the answer.

Who did Brad kiss?
dad   mom

What did Brad do?
read a book   watched TV

What did Brad put on?
shoes   pyjamas

Where was Brad going?
to bed   to school

Reading Comprehension

Lists

Reading a List

Read. Answer the questions.

milk

eggs

bread

apples

bananas

sugar

cheese

Circle the answer.

What kind of writing is this?
a letter   a list

How many items are there?
7   9

How many fruits are there?
3   2

Are chips one of the words?
yes   no

What else might you add?

Notes

Reading a Note

Read. Answer the questions.

> Dad,
> I am on my bike. I went to the school.
> Ali and Jared are with me.
>   Back soon,
>   Sarah

Circle the answer.

What kind of writing is this?
invitation   note

Did they walk to the school?
yes   no

How many people went bike riding?
2   3

Who wrote the note?
Sarah   Dad

What else could you add to the note?

_____

_____

Invitations

Reading an Invitation

Read. Look at the picture.
Answer the questions.

Party Celebration!

What: Zahra's 8th
birthday party

Where: Community Pool

Date: August 10

Time: 1:00 pm

Circle the answer.

What kind of party is it?
Mother's Day   birthday

Who is the party for?
Malik   Zahra

What date is the party on?
1:00 pm   August 10

How old is Zahra?
6 years old   8 years old

What would you take to the party besides a present?

_____

- -

Boxes

Reading a Box

Read. Look at the picture.
Answer the questions.

<u>Underline</u> the right answer.

What is this box advertising?
bird food   dog food

How often should a bird be fed?
twice a day

once a day

A parrot is what type of animal?
bird   snake

What else does a bird need to survive?

_____

_____

_____

Comic Strips

The Lemonade Stand

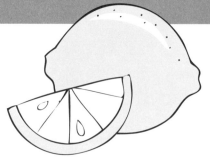

Read. Look at the pictures. Answer the questions.

<u>Underline</u> the right answer.

What form of writing is this?

poem   comic

How much did the lemonade cost?

25¢   10¢

How many glasses of lemonade were sold?

five   eight

What might the child do with the money?

_____

_____

Poetry

Reading Poetry

Read. Look at the pictures. Answer the questions.

In the winter, we wait
for snow,
Then it's off to the hill we go,

We walk up with our sled
and a hat on our head,

Down the hill we slide,
For a quick and snowy ride.

<u>Underline</u> the right answer.

What form of writing is this?

poem   story

What is this writing about?

skating   tobogganing

Which word rhymes
with slide?

ride   head

Which word rhymes
with go?

sled   snow

35

Riddles

Reading Riddles

Read. Look at the pictures. Answer the questions

What Am I?

I stand there waiting
day and night.
My string net hangs from
my hoop.
I wait for orange balls to
be tossed my way.

What am I?

 Circle the right answer.

What form of writing is this?
poem   riddle

- - - - - - - - - - - - - - -

What is this writing about?
a basketball   a basketball net

- - - - - - - - - - - - - - -

What hangs from me?
wooden net   string net

- - - - - - - - - - - - - - -

What do I wait to be tossed
my way?
yellow balls   orange balls

Finding Details

Look for Details

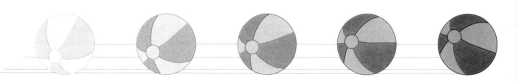

Read. Look at the pictures. Complete the sentences.

My Bouncy Ball

My ball can bounce.
It may roll away, but I will get it.
My ball is red and blue.
I like to play ball with my friends.

Fill in the blanks.

The _____ can bounce.

The colours of the ball are _____ and _____.

I like to play with my _____.

My ball may _____ away.

Story Sequence

What Happened First, Next, Then, and Last

Look at the pictures. Print the number 1, 2, 3, or 4 in the box to put them in order. The first one is started.

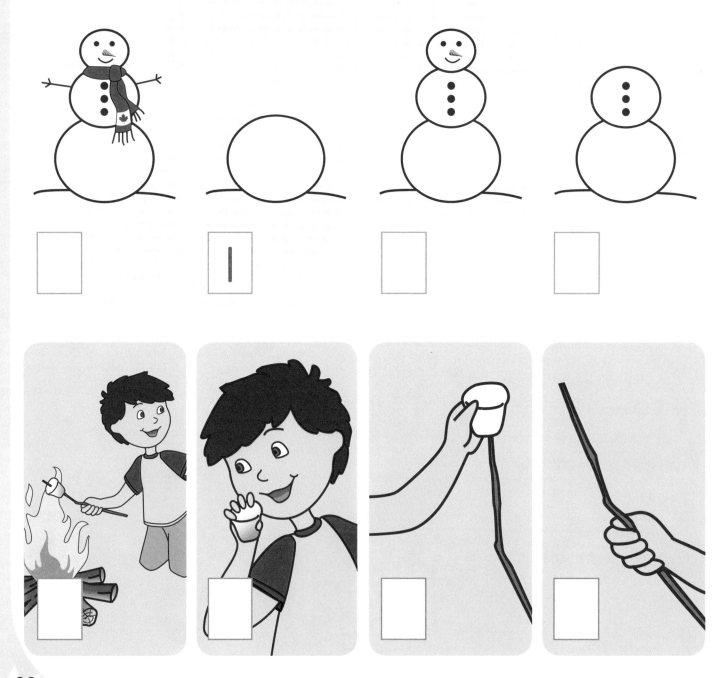

Story Sequence

Order of Steps

Read the steps.
Look at the pictures.
Write the numbers
1, 2, 3, or 4 in
each circle to show
the steps.

How to Make a Chocolate Sundae!

What You Need:

ice cream, chocolate sauce, whipped cream,
cherry, bowl, scoop, spoon

Steps:

1. Scoop ice cream into a bowl.
2. Pour some chocolate sauce on top of the ice cream.
3. Put some whipped cream on the chocolate sauce.
4. Put a cherry on top.
5. Eat and enjoy!

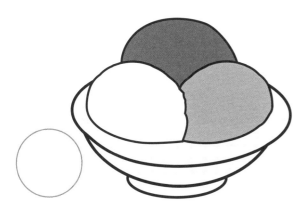

Picture Clues

What's Missing?

Look at the paragraph. Print the missing initial letters in the blanks. Use the Picture Word Bank to help you. Read the completed paragraph.

The Zoo

We went to the zoo. I saw ____iraffes, ____heetahs, and many

____onkeys. A ____ookeeper takes care of the animals. She

feeds the ____olar bears ____ish. The animals sleep in the

____un. It is fun to go to the ____oo.

Picture Word Bank

polar bear   giraffe   zookeeper   sun   cheetah   fish   monkey   zoo

Picture Clues

Read the Story to Find Details

First, read the story. Then read the questions. (Circle) the correct picture to answer each question. Last, colour the pictures.

Making Cookies

My mom made some cookies. She put them in the oven to bake. They smelled good.
I ate two cookies and they were yummy.

What was baked?	Who baked them?	Where were they baked?

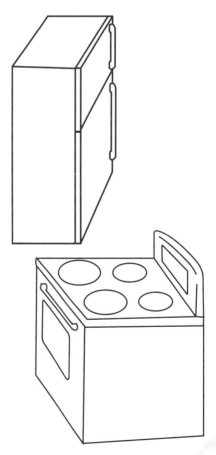

Following Directions

Drawing a Butterfly

Read the steps. Follow the steps to draw the butterfly in the box.

1. Draw an oval for the body.

2. Add a circle on top of the oval for the head.

3. Draw a backward "B" on the left side of the oval for one wing.

4. Draw a proper "B" on the right side of the oval for another wing.

5. Put two antennae on the head.

6. Add eyes and a mouth.

7. Colour your butterfly.

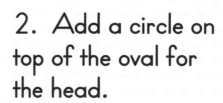

Book Covers

Reading the Cover of a Book

A book cover tells:
- Title (idea of what the book is about)
- Author (who wrote the book)
- Illustrator (who drew the pictures)

Look at the book cover.
Answer the questions.

Who wrote this book?

_____

_____

Who drew the pictures
in the book?

_____

_____

What is the book about?

_____

_____

Signs

Reading Neighbourhood Signs

Read. Answer the questions.

LEMONADE STAND

Saturday July 7th
10:00am to noon

homemade lemonade ✳ cookies
candy ✳ surprises

What time does the lemonade sale begin?

_____

_____

How long is the stand open?

_____

_____

On what day will the stand be open?

_____

_____

What kinds of things can you buy at the lemonade stand?

_____

_____

What might a "surprise" be?

_____

_____

Story Order

Read the story.

Swimming Lessons

Today was my first swimming lesson. We walked to the pool. I put my bathing suit on. I met my teacher. We jumped in the water. It was fun!

Rewrite the sentences below in the correct order.

I put my bathing suit on.	We walked to the pool.
We jumped in the water.	I met my teacher.

1. _____

2. _____

3. _____

4. _____

Story Order

Read the story.

Henry's Birthday

Henry's birthday party is today. He is 6 years old. First, he and his pals played games. Then they had pizza and cupcakes for lunch. Last, they sang "Happy Birthday."

Rewrite the sentences below in the correct order.

Last, they sang "Happy Birthday."

First, they played games.

Today is Henry's birthday.

Then they had lunch.

1. _____

2. _____

3. _____

4. _____

Story Details

Finding Story Details

Read the story. Answer the questions.

My friend Alex and I like to swim after lunch. We go to the lake or pool. We jump in the water, play tag, or have races. Alex likes to blow bubbles. There are many rules to follow when we go swimming. Swimming is excellent exercise.

What is my friend's name?

_____

_____

Where do we like to swim?

_____

_____

What does Alex like to do in the water?

_____

_____

When do we like to swim?

_____

_____

What are some swimming rules?

_____

_____

Character

Describing Characters in a Story

Read the story.
Answer the questions.

Best Friends

Sam and Tara are best friends. They are in the same class. They like the same games. They both love dogs. Both girls have brown hair. Sam has one sister. Tara has two brothers. Sam and Tara play badminton in the gym every Saturday.

What do Sam and Tara both like?

_____

_____

_____

How are the girls different?

_____

_____

_____

What do they do every Saturday?

_____

_____

Visualizing Characters

Best Friends

Draw a picture of Sam and
Tara playing badminton.

Story Details

Finding Story Details

Read the story. Answer the questions in complete sentences.

Trains

Trains can be long. They go very fast. Some trains carry people. Some trains are very loud. Trains ride on tracks.

Are trains fast or slow?

_____

_____

What do some trains carry?

_____

_____

What do trains ride on?

_____

_____

Can you hear a train?

_____

Use of Words

Fun with Words

Read the story. Answer the questions.

Bugs

Small ones, big ones, thin ones, fat ones — bugs are all around. I am frightened and I yell, "Go away!" They creep, slither, and run out of sight. I feel better when I can't see any bugs.

Circle the answer.

In the story, the word "frightened" means:

a. scared   b. happy

c. sad

The word "can't" means:

a. can   b. cannot

c. could

The opposite of "yell" is:

a. sing   b. whisper

c. squeal

Which word does not rhyme with "run"?

a. bun   b. sun

c. rope

The word "bug" is a:

a. noun   b. verb

Facts

Pet Fact Cards

There are many kinds of cards. Some are about sports. These cards are about house pets.

The front of the fact card has a picture so we know what the pet looks like.

The back of the card has facts.

HAMSTERS
- Hamsters live in cages. They like tunnels and wheels in their cage.
- Hamsters eat seeds, vegetables, and hamster treats.
- Hamsters are nocturnal. They sleep during the day and are awake at night.

Facts

Finding Facts

Look at the card.
Did you notice the
fish bowl?
Can you see the fins?
Do you see the tail?

Answer the questions.

GOLDFISH

HOUSEHOLD PETS

GOLDFISH
• Goldfish live in a fish bowl or an aquarium.
• There are 500 types of goldfish.
• Goldfish eat flakes of food.
• Goldfish have colourful bodies.
• Goldfish like to live in groups.

What facts did you learn about
the goldfish?

_____

- -

_____

- -

_____

Would you like a goldfish for a pet? Why or why not?

_____

- -

_____

_____

_____

Conflict or Problem

Identify the Problem

Read the story. Answer the questions in complete sentences.

Going to the Beach

Tom went to the beach with his friend Samir. They played in the sand with an orange pail. Waves came up on the beach and took the orange pail out into the water. Tom was upset. Samir went into the water to get the bucket. Tom put the bucket far from the waves.

What is the problem or conflict in the story?

_____

_____

_____

_____

How was the problem solved?

_____

_____

_____

_____

Personal Connection

Making a Connection to the Story

Read the story. Think about a time when you were scared. Answer the questions in complete sentences.

At the Park

Shelby went to the park with her mom. She played on the swings. Her mom pushed her too high. Shelby got scared and started to cry. Shelby's mom stopped the swing and gave her a hug.

What has scared you?

_____

_____

_____

_____

What made you feel better?

_____

_____

_____

```
R F A T E O F A N D
F T F H W E O Y O U
E O W I T H B Y I S
O O I E H T H A T S
T H E O N S E E I T
T N H E I N A R E I
I T E F O R N B E W
R A S D W A S A I O
E S H I S T T O A N
R W A S O R T H E T
```

Find these words:

AND	BE	HIS	OF	THAT	WE
ARE	BY	IN	ON	THE	WITH
AS	FOR	IS	OR	TO	YOU
AT	HE	IT	SEE	WAS	

```
I M Y C O M E A L L
C H A D A S A I D H
N O O L O O K C A N
I N O T W H A T A T
O S H E T H E Y U K
T E I N T O H A V E
M A N B U T H I S O
W H E N W E R E L I
L T D O S O M E U P
C L I K E E S A W S
```

Find these words:

ALL	COME	INTO	NO	SHE	THIS	WHEN
AN	DO	LIKE	NOT	SO	UP	
BUT	HAD	LOOK	SAID	SOME	WERE	
CAN	HAVE	MY	SAW	THEY	WHAT	

```
A M T H E M C A M E
I E W O U L D E L C
E W Y E S M A K E L
D O W N T H E N N E
E E O U T C O U L D
H E R E W E N T E N
W T T H E R E T T U
D I F W I L L G O O
R H E R L I T T L E
M W A N T G E T E E
```

Find these words:

AM	DOWN	HER	LITTLE	THEM	WANT	WOULD
CAME	GET	HERE	MAKE	THEN	WENT	YES
COULD	GO	IF	OUT	THERE	WILL	

Solutions

Letters, Sounds, and Words
Initial Sounds
Initial sounds are what we hear at the beginning of words.
Say each letter. Say the sound each letter makes.
Circle the letter that make the initial sound for each picture.

(Aa) Ll Rr (Ff) Hh Tt

(Tt) Gg Oo (Dd) Ee (Kk)

Nn (Ss) Ii (Rr) Pp (Mm)

Page 2

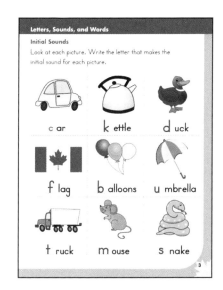

Letters, Sounds, and Words
Initial Sounds
Look at each picture. Write the letter that makes the
initial sound for each picture.

c ar   k ettle   d uck

f lag   b alloons   u mbrella

t ruck   m ouse   s nake

Page 3

Letters, Sounds, and Words
Final Sounds
Final sounds are what we hear at the end of words.
Look at each picture. Write the letter that makes the
final sound for each picture.

ice crea m   bal l   hamburge r

boo k   carro t   yo-y o

be e   octopu s   trai n

Page 4

Letters, Sounds, and Words
Scrambled Letters
Unscramble the word. Write the word on the line.

n a f   fan   i g p   pig

r c a   car   g b u   bug

t a b   bat   p m a   map

t n e   ten   a c t   cat

Page 5

Letters, Sounds, and Words
Plurals
Words that refer to more than one of something are plurals.
Look at the pictures. Write the plural words.
Use the Plural Word List if you need help.

Plural Word List
dogs   balls   apples   crayons   trees   frogs

apples   crayons

trees   dogs

frogs   balls

Page 6

Letters, Sounds, and Words
Picture Clues
Pictures help you!
Read the sentence. Circle the word that
makes sense. Then, write the word.

Mom is at the   park
(park) plant

I ride in a   car
(car) cat

I sit on a   chair
sofa (chair)

I ride in a   bus
(bus) box

Dad has a   boat
bike (boat)

Page 7

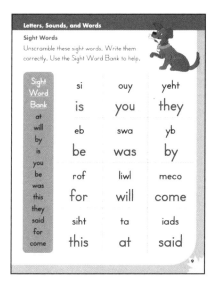

Letters, Sounds, and Words
Sight Words
Unscramble these sight words. Write them
correctly. Use the Sight Word Bank to help.

Sight Word Bank
at
will
by
is
you
be
was
this
they
said
for
come

si   is   ouy   you   yeht   they

eb   be   swa   was   yb   by

rof   for   liwl   will   meco   come

siht   this   ta   at   iads   said

Page 9

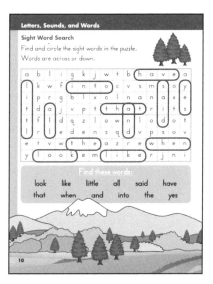

Letters, Sounds, and Words
Sight Word Search
Find and circle the sight words in the puzzle.
Words are across or down.

Find these words:
look   like   little   all   said   have
that   when   and   into   the   yes

Page 10

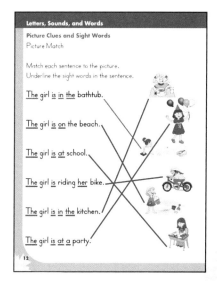

Letters, Sounds, and Words
Picture Clues and Sight Words
Picture Match

Match each sentence to the picture.
Underline the sight words in the sentence.

The girl is in the bathtub.

The girl is on the beach.

The girl is at school.

The girl is riding her bike.

The girl is in the kitchen.

The girl is at a party.

Page 12

59

Solutions

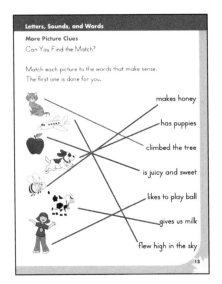

Letters, Sounds, and Words
More Picture Clues
Can You Find the Match?

Match each picture to the words that make sense.
The first one is done for you.

- makes honey
- has puppies
- climbed the tree
- is juicy and sweet
- likes to play ball
- gives us milk
- flew high in the sky

Page 13

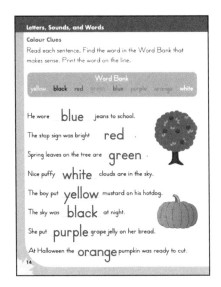

Letters, Sounds, and Words
Colour Clues

Read each sentence. Find the word in the Word Bank that makes sense. Print the word on the line.

Word Bank
yellow · black · red · green · blue · purple · orange · white

He wore **blue** jeans to school.

The stop sign was bright **red**.

Spring leaves on the tree are **green**.

Nice puffy **white** clouds are in the sky.

The boy put **yellow** mustard on his hotdog.

The sky was **black** at night.

She put **purple** grape jelly on her bread.

At Halloween the **orange** pumpkin was ready to cut.

Page 14

Letters, Sounds, and Words
Rhyming
Rhyming Words

Read each sentence. Do you hear the two rhyming words?
Underline the words that rhyme.

The <u>hat</u> was on the <u>cat</u>.

I can <u>bake</u> a <u>cake</u>.

She ate a <u>bun</u> in the <u>sun</u>.

There is a <u>bug</u> on the <u>rug</u>.

The <u>pig</u> is wearing a <u>wig</u>.

The <u>frog</u> jumped on a <u>log</u>.

Page 15

Letters, Sounds, and Words
Rhyming
More Rhyming Words

Fill in the blanks with words that rhyme with the underlined word. Use the pictures as clues.

The **man** drove a delivery van.

The boy hit his head when he fell off the **bed**.

After school, I swam in the **pool**.

With my **pen**, I print the number ten.

I skinned my **knee** climbing a tree.

Page 16

Letters, Sounds, and Words
Detail Words
Who or What?

Detail Words like "who" or "what" provide information. The circled words tell us "who" or "what." Print "who" or "what" on each line.

(My dad) is at home. **who**

Children love to eat (candy). **what**

The girl got new (shoes). **what**

The (magician) did neat tricks. **who**

(Farrah and her friend) went to the park. **who**

(The car) drove on the road. **what**

(The bird) flew to the tree. **what**

Page 17

Letters, Sounds, and Words
Detail Words
When or Where?

Detail Words like "when" or "where" provide information. The circled words tell us "when" or "where." Print "when" or "where" on each line.

On (Halloween), I get candy. **when**

The milk is (in the fridge). **where**

(Tomorrow), we go to school. **when**

The pig rolled (in the mud). **where**

The hat is (on his head). **where**

In (December), it will snow. **when**

On (Monday), I go swimming. **when**

Page 18

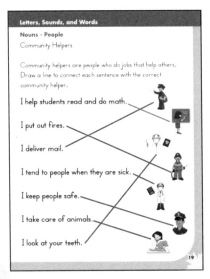

Letters, Sounds, and Words
Nouns · People
Community Helpers

Community helpers are people who do jobs that help others. Draw a line to connect each sentence with the correct community helper.

- I help students read and do math.
- I put out fires.
- I deliver mail.
- I tend to people when they are sick.
- I keep people safe.
- I take care of animals.
- I look at your teeth.

Page 19

Letters, Sounds, and Words
Nouns · Objects
Pick an Object

Read the sentences. Look at the pictures. Print the sentence number in the box to show which object goes with each sentence.

1. Print your name with this.
2. Eat ice cream with this.
3. Cut paper with this.
4. Boil water in this.
5. Watch your favourite show on this.
6. Make your hair neat with this.
7. Cut an apple with this.
8. Put in a nail with this.

3 **2** **1** **7**
4 **6** **5** **8**

Page 20

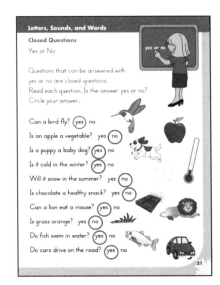

Letters, Sounds, and Words
Closed Questions
Yes or No

Questions that can be answered with yes or no are closed questions. Read each question. Is the answer yes or no? Circle your answer.

Can a bird fly? (yes) no

Is an apple a vegetable? yes (no)

Is a puppy a baby dog? (yes) no

Is it cold in the winter? (yes) no

Will it snow in the summer? yes (no)

Is chocolate a healthy snack? yes (no)

Can a lion eat a mouse? (yes) no

Is grass orange? yes (no)

Do fish swim in water? (yes) no

Do cars drive on the road? (yes) no

Page 21

Solutions

Reading Comprehension

Sentences

Choose the Best Sentence

Read each sentence. Select the sentence that best describes the picture. Underline the sentence.

The toys are a mess.
Dad put the toys away.
The teddy bear, clown, and car are in the toy box.

The girl is going to school.
The girl loves the bath.
The girl is going to bed.

The boy is going swimming.
The boy is playing in the sand.
The boy has a ball.

22

Page 22

Reading Comprehension

Sentences

Picture Match

Look at each picture. Read each sentence. Match each sentence with the best picture.

This keeps you warm.
This protects you from the sun.
This is a sport cap.

These have Velcro.
These have laces.
These are blue.

This ball is for kicking.
This ball is for hitting with a bat.
This ball is for playing in a pool.

23

Page 23

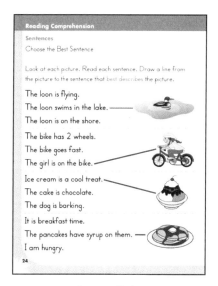

Reading Comprehension

Sentences

Choose the Best Sentence

Look at each picture. Read each sentence. Draw a line from the picture to the sentence that best describes the picture.

The loon is flying.
The loon swims in the lake.
The loon is on the shore.

The bike has 2 wheels.
The bike goes fast.
The girl is on the bike.

Ice cream is a cool treat.
The cake is chocolate.

The dog is barking.
It is breakfast time.
The pancakes have syrup on them.
I am hungry.

24

Page 24

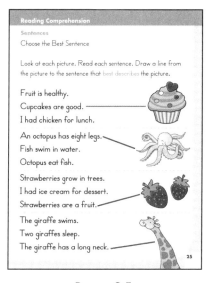

Reading Comprehension

Sentences

Choose the Best Sentence

Look at each picture. Read each sentence. Draw a line from the picture to the sentence that best describes the picture.

Fruit is healthy.
Cupcakes are good.
I had chicken for lunch.

An octopus has eight legs.
Fish swim in water.
Octopus eat fish.

Strawberries grow in trees.
I had ice cream for dessert.
Strawberries are a fruit.

The giraffe swims.
Two giraffes sleep.
The giraffe has a long neck.

25

Page 25

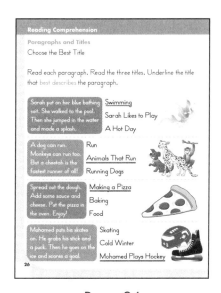

Reading Comprehension

Paragraphs and Titles

Choose the Best Title

Read each paragraph. Read the three titles. Underline the title that best describes the paragraph.

Sarah put on her blue bathing suit. She walked to the pool. Then she jumped in the water and made a splash.
Swimming
Sarah Likes to Play
A Hot Day

A dog can run. Monkeys can run too. But a cheetah is the fastest runner of all!
Run
Animals That Run
Running Dogs

Spread out the dough. Add some sauce and cheese. Put the pizza in the oven. Enjoy!
Making a Pizza
Baking
Food

Mohamed puts his skates on. He grabs his stick and a puck. Then he goes on the ice and scores a goal.
Skating
Cold Winter
Mohamed Plays Hockey

26

Page 26

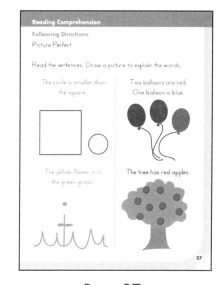

Reading Comprehension

Following Directions

Picture Perfect

Read the sentences. Draw a picture to explain the words.

The circle is smaller than the square.

Two balloons are red. One balloon is blue.

The yellow flower is in the green grass.

The tree has red apples.

27

Page 27

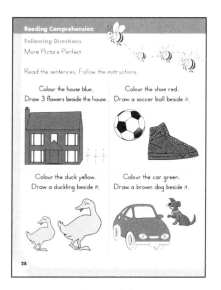

Reading Comprehension

Following Directions

More Picture Perfect

Read the sentences. Follow the instructions.

Colour the house blue. Draw 3 flowers beside the house.

Colour the shoe red. Draw a soccer ball beside it.

Colour the duck yellow. Draw a duckling beside it.

Colour the car green. Draw a brown dog beside it.

28

Page 28

Reading Comprehension

Picture Clues

Reading with Picture Clues

Read the story. Use the pictures to help you. Answer the questions.

Brad brushed his teeth.
He put his pyjamas on.
He read a book.
Brad kissed his mom.
He turned out the light.

Circle the answer.

Who did Brad kiss?
dad (mom)

What did Brad do?
(read a book) watched TV

What did Brad put on?
shoes (pyjamas)

Where was Brad going?
(to bed) to school

29

Page 29

Reading Comprehension

Lists

Reading a List

Read. Answer the questions.

milk
eggs
bread
apples
bananas
sugar
cheese

Circle the answer.

What kind of writing is this?
a letter (a list)

How many items are there?
(7) 9

How many fruits are there?
3 (2)

Are chips one of the words?
yes (no)

What else might you add?

Answers will vary.

30

Page 30

Solutions

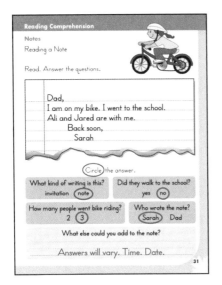

Page 31

Page 32

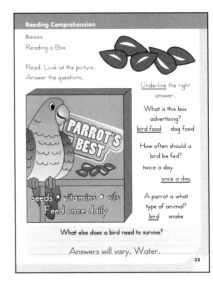

Page 33

Page 34

Page 35

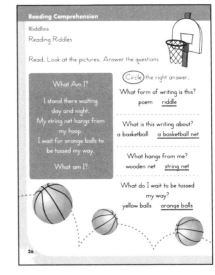

Page 36

Page 37

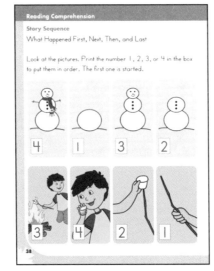

Page 38

Page 39

Solutions

Page 40

Page 41

Page 43

Page 44

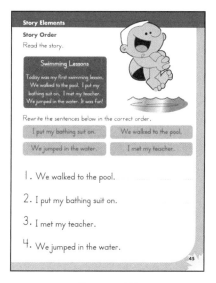

Page 45

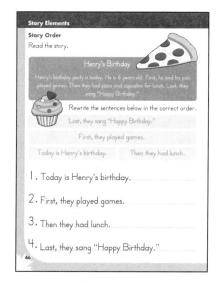

Page 46

Page 47

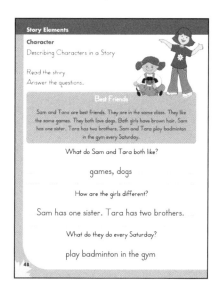

Page 48

Page 50

63

Solutions

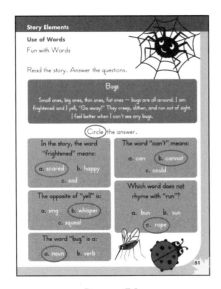

Page 51

Page 53

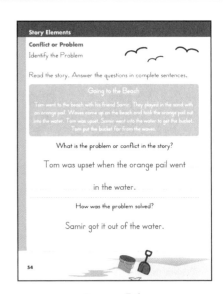

Page 54

Page 56

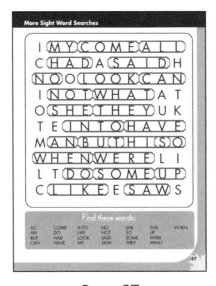

Page 57

Page 58

Written by teachers working in the Canadian classroom

Writing

Grade 1

PARTY!

A+

- Printing practice and alphabet activities
- Punctuation and grammar
- Sight words
- Writing activities
- And much more!

D. J. Whitlock, B.Ed.

Grade 1 Writing

Contents

Print **a** and **A**.

a a a a a a a a

A A A A A A A A

Print the letter **a** under each thing that starts with the **a** sound.

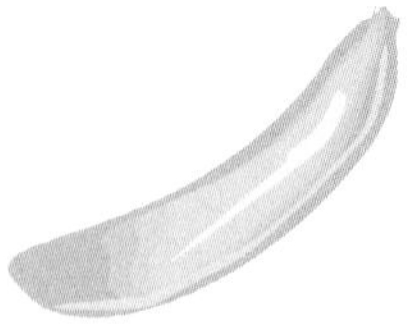

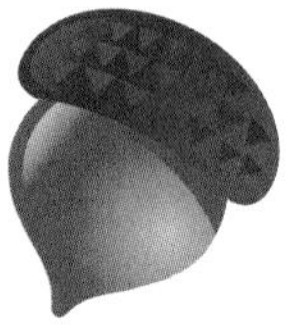

_____ _____ _____ _____ _____

Print **b** and **B**.

b b b b b b b b

B B B B B B B B

Colour the things that begin with the **b** sound.

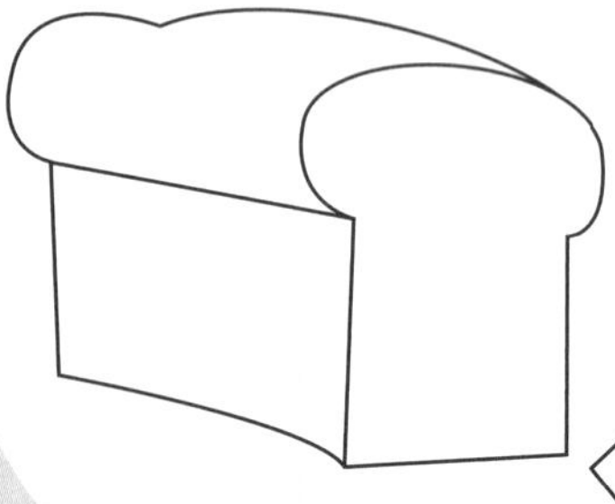

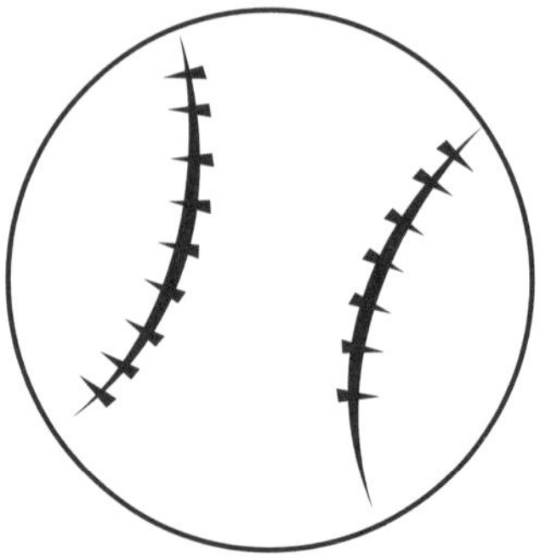

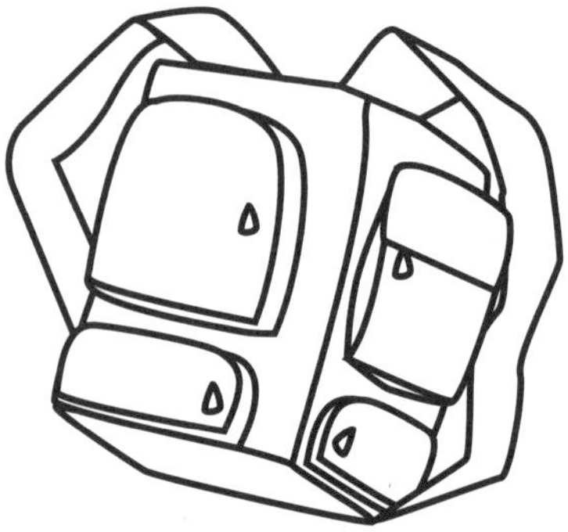

Print **c** and **C**.

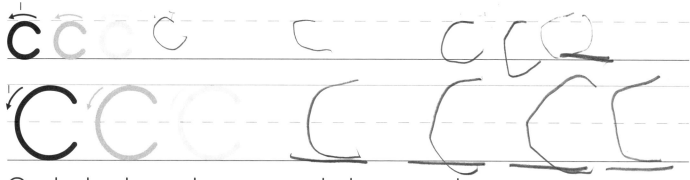

Circle the things that start with the **c** sound.

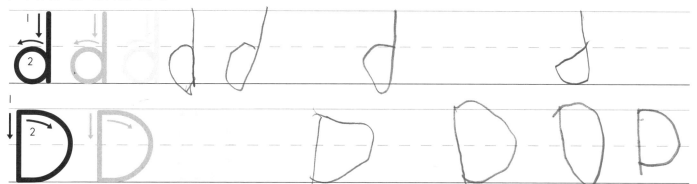

Print **d** and **D**.

Find these **d** words.

duck

dog

door

day

doll

do

d	d	d	o	g
o	a	u	u	d
o	y	c	c	o
r	a	k	w	o
d	o	l	l	d

Print **e** and **E**.

Unscramble the letters to spell words that begin with the letter **e**.

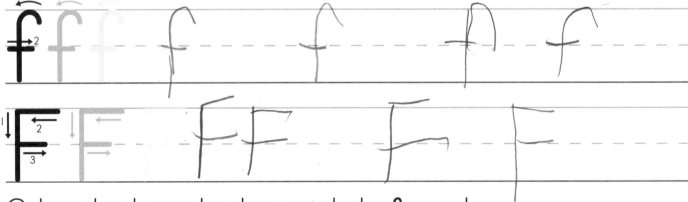

sgeg	lfe	aet	eey	rae

Print **f** and **F**.

Colour the things that begin with the **f** sound.

Print **g** and **G**.

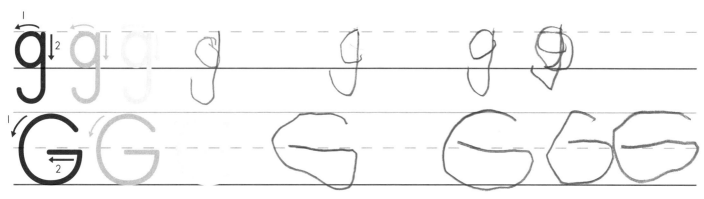

Draw a line from the **g** in the middle to each thing that starts with the **g** sound. One is done for you.

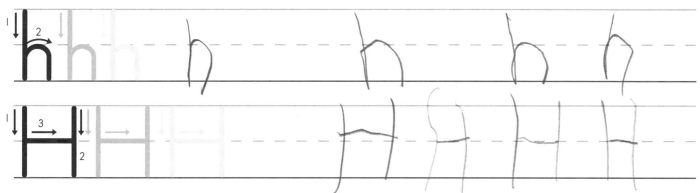

Print **h** and **H**.

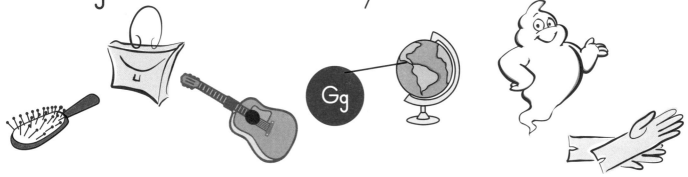

Circle the things that begin with the **h** sound.

Print i and I.

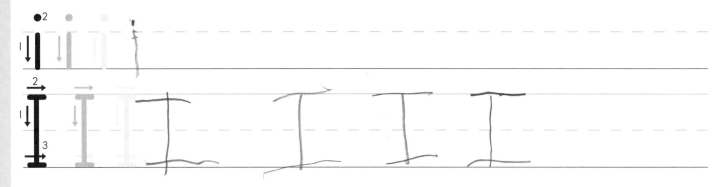

Print: Iris is interested in insects.

Print j and J.

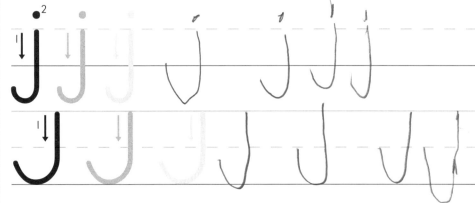

Circle the things that begin with the j sound.

Printing, Letters, Sounds and Words

Print **k** and **K**.

Draw a line from the **k** in the middle to each thing that starts with the **k** sound.

Print **l** and **L**.

Circle the things that begin with the **l** sound.

Print **m** and **M**.

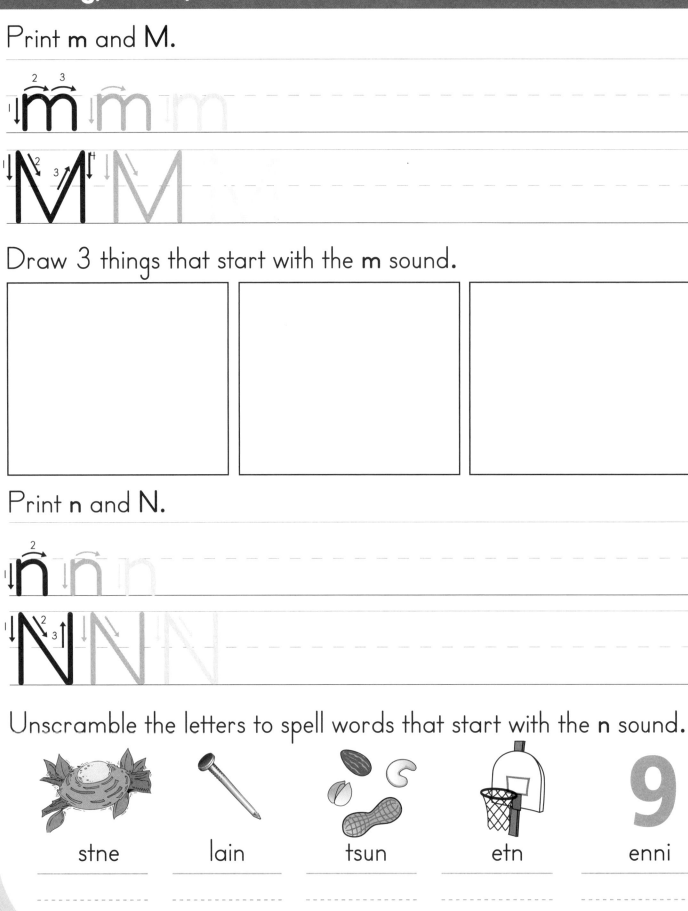

Draw 3 things that start with the **m** sound.

Print **n** and **N**.

Unscramble the letters to spell words that start with the **n** sound.

stne   lain   tsun   etn   enni

Print **o** and O.

O O O

O O O

Print: Olivia opens oranges on her own.

Print **p** and P.

p p p

P P P

Colour the pictures that begin with the **p** sound.

9

Print q and Q.

Print r and R.

Find these q words:

e	o	q	n	q	e	n	u
i	n	u	c	e	k	t	q
n	o	i	t	s	e	u	q
o	e	l	n	e	a	u	e
i	u	t	k	c	i	a	q
k	e	i	k	e	t	c	c
c	n	k	t	u	n	e	i
i	n	e	k	k	i	n	u

queen
quack
quilt
quiet
question

Print r and R.

Circle things that start with the r sound.

10

Print **s** and S.

S s s

S S S

Draw 3 things that start with the **s** sound.

Print **t** and T.

t t t

T T T

Colour things that start with the **t** sound.

Print **u** and U.

Print **v** and V.

Print **w** and W.

Print **x** and X.

Print y and y.

Print z and Z.

Find these **u, v, w, x, y,** and **z** words:

n	m	w	e	o	l	y	o	o
o	i	o	y	d	o	o	a	y
l	i	l	w	y	o	u	u	m
e	o	l	o	z	z	n	n	w
m	z	e	d	i	e	g	d	p
r	r	y	n	p	v	b	e	y
e	u	o	i	p	y	a	r	x
t	a	l	w	e	e	m	n	a
a	l	l	e	r	b	m	u	o
w	l	a	w	z	e	p	o	w

umbrella
watermelon
yoyo
van
zebra
xray
yam
violin
zipper
worm
under
yellow
zoo
window
young

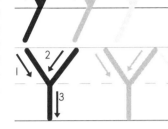

Alphabet Fill in the Blanks

Print the missing **lowercase** letters in the peacock feathers.

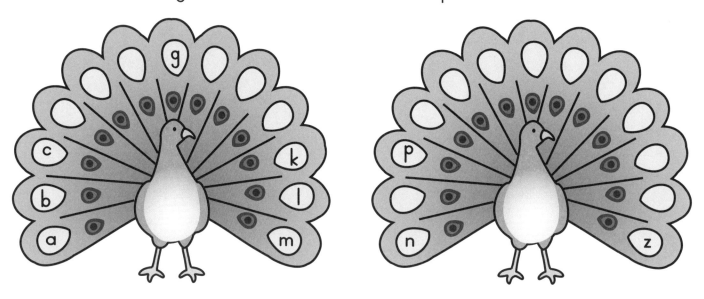

Print the missing **uppercase** letters on the beads.

Days of the Week   Trace and print.

Sunday

Monday

Tuesday

Wednesday

Thursday

Friday

Saturday

Colour each balloon to match the colour word.

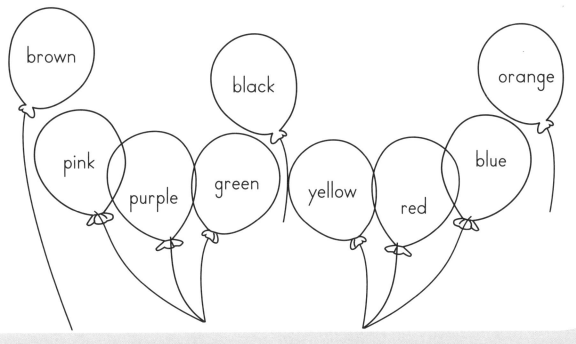

brown

black

orange

pink

purple

green

yellow

red

blue

Initial Sounds

Initial sounds come at the **beginning** of words.

Circle the letter that makes the beginning sound for each picture.

| l f t | n h m | d c b | b f k |
| g h k | o a c | n r m | d c b |

Draw a line from each letter to the picture that begins
with that sound.

p

s

b

l

m

f

g

Initial Sounds

Print the letter that makes the **beginning** sound for each picture.

Print the letter that makes the **beginning** sound for each picture.

_____un

_____hale

_____gg

_____iolin

_____am

_____ray

_____ebra

_____range

17

Final Sounds

Circle the **ending** sound for each picture.

| t e h c | a g j y | g t c n | h d o b |
| o b p d | s r t a | d n k h | w v x i |

Circle the pictures in each row that **end** with the given sound.

K

S

Blends

When 2 or more consonants go together they make a blend.
Say the name of each picture. Print the consonants that make
the beginning blend for each word.

fl   cl   gl   bl   dr   cr   tr   br   sp   str

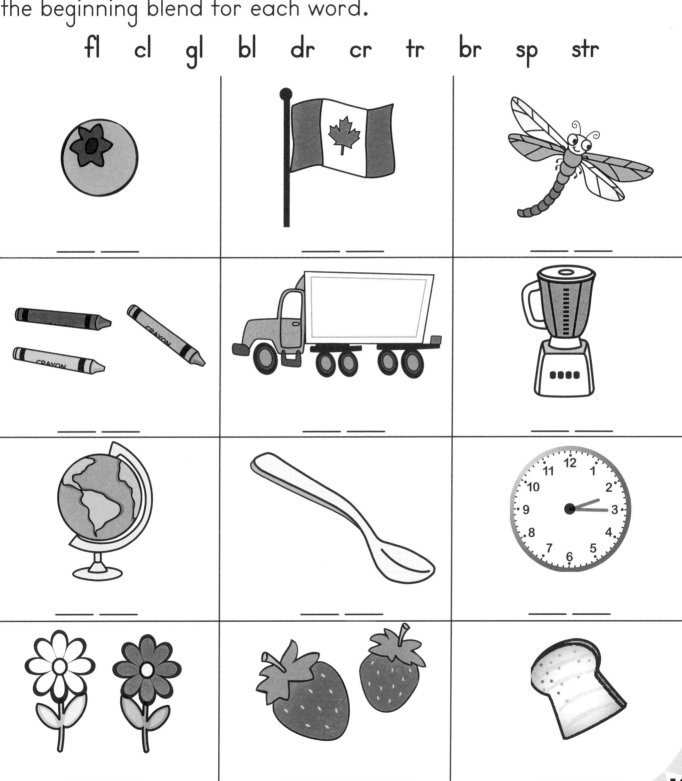

____   ____   ____

____   ____   ____

____   ____   ____

____   ____   ____

Long Vowel Sounds

The letters a, e, i, o, and u are vowels.

Long vowel sounds say their own name.

For example: Long a is the sound in **snake**

Put an X on the pictures that have the same long vowel sound as the letter in that row.

Long Vowel Sounds a e i o u

Print the long vowel to complete the words.

b ____ at

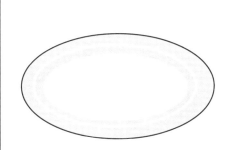

pl ____ te

____ ce cream

p ____ e

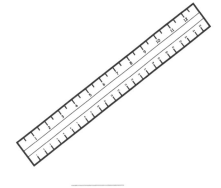

r ____ ler

l ____ af

p ____ as

f ____ ve

t ____ re

21

Short Vowel Sounds

Short vowel sounds are those you hear in **p**at, **p**et, **p**it, **p**ot, and **p**utt. Circle the pictures that have the same short vowel sound as the letter.

a

e

i

o

u

Add the Missing Short Vowel Sounds

Write the short vowel to complete the words.

c ____ p

p ____ n

fr ____ g

s ____ x

f ____ n

b ____ g

b ____ g

t ____ n

l ____ ck

23

It Takes Two — Compound Words

Two words can be put together to make a new word with its own meaning.

➡ Example:

rain + bow =  rainbow

snow + ball = _____

lip + stick = _____

pop + corn = _____

foot + ball = _____

Rhyme

Rhyming words are words that sound alike at the end of the word.

⇨ Example: cat and hat

Draw lines to match the pictures that rhyme.

Write the word that rhymes.

 hat

 bed

 toy

chips

_____

_____

_____

_____

Antonyms

Antonyms are words that have **opposite meanings**.
Draw lines to match the words that are antonyms.

add	off
big	in
out	subtract
stop	go
on	small
night	day
float	sink

More Antonyms

Circle the word that is the opposite of the one on the left.

left	right up
up	top down
under	over near
cold	cool hot
bad	good red
sink	float drop

Alphabetical Order is the order in which the letters come in the alphabet. Connect the dots. Follow **abc** order.

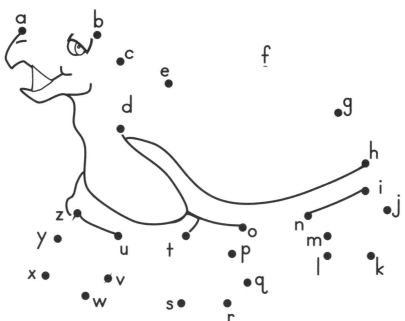

Circle the first letter of each word.

Print each pair of words in alphabetical order.

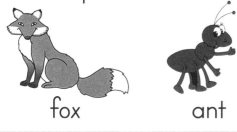

fox   ant

_____

_____

snail   pan

_____

_____

loon   frog

_____

_____

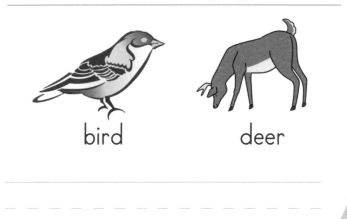

bird   deer

_____

_____

Plurals

Words that name more than one thing are called plurals.

Many words add **s** to name more than one.

➡ Example: dog   dogs

Sort the words.

One	Plurals — More Than One

apple

flowers

fish

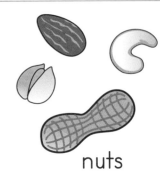

nuts

bees

book

skates

Telling Sentences

All sentences begin with a **capital letter**.
Telling **sentences** end with a period.

➡ Example: The car is red.

Read each sentence.
Print it on the line using a capital and a period.

the bat is on the mat _____

_____

my bike is nice _____

_____

the fish is gold _____

_____

my bed is big _____

Circle the correct sentence.

the frog is green

the frog is green.

The frog is green.

Asking Sentences

Asking sentences end with a question mark (?).

⇨ Example: Is the pizza hot?

Read each asking sentence.
Print it on the line using a capital and a question mark.

⇨ Example: will you play with me

Will you play with me?

is the helmet red

_____

_____

what is your name

_____

_____

Print the first words of each asking sentence on the line. Don't forget
to use a capital letter! End each asking sentence with a question mark.

⇨ Example: ____Do____ you like cake _?_   (do)

_____ I have a cookie please ____ (may)

_____ many spoons do you need ____ (how)

_____ you sing ____ (will)

Exclamation Sentences

Exclamation sentences tell something exciting or surprising or shows someone is shouting. They end with an exclamation mark!

⇨ Example: I won a prize!

Read each sentence. Print the first word of each sentence on the line. Don't forget to use a capital letter! End each exclamation sentence with an exclamation mark.

⇨ Example: _____I_____ broke my leg _!_
                i

_____
   help

_____ won _____
   we

Ouch! _____ tea is hot _____
        this

Circle the correct sentence.

my dog is lost
My dog is lost
My dog is lost!

Horray! my dog is found
Hooray! My dog is found.
Hooray! My dog is found!

Grammar and Punctuation

Complete the final punctuation. Use . ? or !

1. How old are you____
2. I like to eat chocolate ice cream____
3. My favourite food is pizza____
4. What did you do on your vacation____
5. How fast did you run____
6. My dog can play catch with me____
7. I got an A on my last math test____
8. Does your teacher give you homework____
9. The weather today is sunny and bright____
10. I want to have a fish for a pet____
11. Who is your best friend____
12. My friend Mei Lei and I like to play soccer____
13. We won first prize____

Imagine you went to a birthday party.
Make up 2 telling sentences about the party.

1. _____

2. _____

Nouns

Nouns are naming words for **people, places** or things.
Animals are nouns too!

Print the nouns in the correct box.

 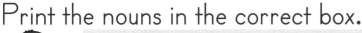

boy	yo-yo	mother	leaf
key	girl	book	park
iron	school	home	quilt
box	puck	vet	pal

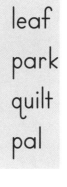

Person    Place    Thing

_____   _____   _____

_____   _____   _____

_____   _____   _____

_____   _____   _____

_____   _____   _____

_____   _____   _____

_____   _____   _____

33

Verbs

Verbs are **action words** that tell what someone or something does.

1. The kids _____ laps together.

2. The boy _____ into the pool.

3. The woman _____ to the girl.

4. The boys _____ in the water.

5. The girl _____ for her goggles.

6. A boy _____ on the side.

Nouns and Verbs

Read each sentence. Underline the nouns in green.
Circle the verbs in **red**.

➡ Example: The <u>girl</u> (rides) fast.

1. The dog eats bones.

2. The pig rolled in the mud.

3. The boy paddles the canoe.

4. The flashlight shines.

Word Sort Print the nouns and verbs in the correct boxes.

dog   teacher   climb   ball   hand   park   fish   pet

hop   bike   dad   dance   stir   skip   sister

Nouns (person, place or thing)   Verbs (action words)

_____   _____

_____   _____

_____   _____

_____   _____

_____   _____

_____   _____

Adjectives

Adjectives are **describing words.** Read the describing words to figure out what the object is.

➪ Example: small cute soft

It is a <u>puppy</u>.

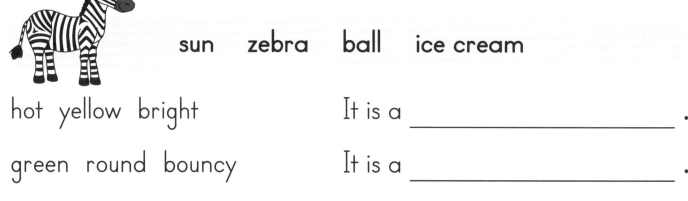

sun   zebra   ball   ice cream

hot yellow bright   It is a _____ .

green round bouncy   It is a _____ .

tasty cold hard   It is _____ .

striped black white   It is a _____ .

List two adjectives to describe each picture.

_____   _____

_____   _____

Adjectives

Adjectives make a sentence more interesting.
Add describing words.

1. A _____ frog is

   sitting on a _____ rock.

2. The _____ boy likes

   to cook _____ marshmallows.

3. The _____ rabbit

   hops on the _____ grass.

4. The _____ porcupine

   walks slowly.

5. Six _____ ants sit on

   the _____ logs.

Sentences

Read the sentence. Follow the directions.

Ali scored a goal today.

1. Underline the word "scored."
2. Circle the word that tells what Ali scored.
3. Put an X on the word that tells who scored a goal.
4. Put a box around when Ali scored a goal.
5. Draw a picture of Ali scoring a goal.

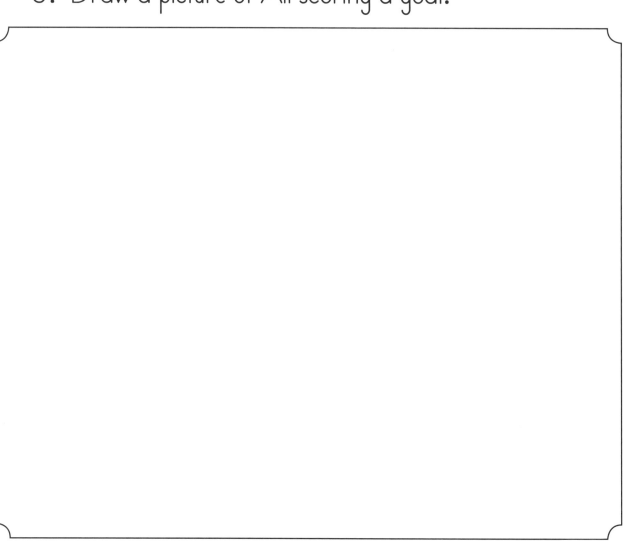

Sentences

Put the words in the correct order. Print the sentence on the line.
Start with a capital letter. End with a period.

slow is snail a

_____

_____

music nice plays man the

_____

_____

swims the the in loon lake

_____

_____

map the check let's

_____

_____

skip to I love

_____

_____

Brainstorming Ideas

Write the words you think of when you see the following pictures.

Sorting Ideas

Draw a line from each thing to the box where it belongs.

moon

plane

fish

helicopter

 sun

cloud

submarine

seagull

octopus

star

loon

lobster

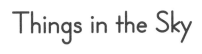

Things in the Sky

Things in the Ocean

Writing Sentences

Write a sentence to tell about each job.

 Veterinarian

_____

 Astronaut

_____

 Zookeeper

_____

 Chef

_____

 Pilot

_____

Writing Labels

Draw your bedroom and label the following parts:

door   window   closet   light
switch   lamp   desk   dresser

Writing a Description

If you could create a new kind of juice, what would it be?
Describe it. Then draw the label.

Descriptive Writing

My Favourite Month. Complete the sentences.

My favourite month is...

_____

- -

_____

I like this month because...

- -

_____

In this month I like to...

- -

_____

Next time my favourite month comes, I hope...

- -

_____

Draw a picture
of what you like
to do this month.

Writing an Invitation

Invite your friend to your birthday. You are going bowling from 2–4 p.m. Fill in the invitation.

To: _____

Bowling Party

_____ is having a party

Place: _____

Date: _____

Time it begins: _____

Time it ends: _____

R.S.V.P. _____

Hint: Tell how to respond to the invitation beside R.S.V.P. This might be your phone number or email address.

Writing a Story

Look at the picture. Write a story about it.

Write a friendly letter

Write a letter to a friend or relative thanking them for a gift.

_____

(Today's date)

_____

(greeting) Dear

Use a capital on the first word! Put a comma after the person's name.

_____

(body) Message you want to send.

_____

_____

_____

_____

_____

_____

(closing) Your friend, or Love,

Use a capital on the first word only. Put a comma at the end.

_____

(your name)

Writing a Story

Every story has a **beginning**, a **middle**, and an **end**.

Think of a fairytale you know. How does it begin? What happens in the middle? How does it end? Write a sentence about each part. Put the title at the top.

_____

(title)

Beginning

_____

_____

_____

_____

Middle

_____

_____

_____

_____

End

_____

_____

_____

_____

Look at the picture. Write sentences about what you see.

➡ Example:
There are eggs
in the pan.

Procedural Writing

Write a sentence that tells what is happening in each picture.

First, _____

_____

_____

Second, _____

_____

_____

Then, _____

_____

_____

Finally, _____

_____

_____

Read the sentences. What comes first? Put numbers beside the other sentences to show the order they happen.

I go to school. _____

I get dressed. _____

I wake up. _____

I brush my teeth. _____

I eat breakfast. _____

First, **next**, and **last** are words that tell the order of what happened in a story. Finish each sentence to tell the order of what happened in the pictures.

First, _____

_____

Next, _____

_____

Last, _____

_____

Writing Speech Bubbles

Speech bubbles in cartoons and comics tell what is being said.

Fill in the Speech bubbles.

Writing Lists

Lists keep us organized. Children like to make lists of their favourite songs, games, sports cards, or dolls. Make two lists.

_____'s Shopping List

_____'s Favourite Toys

Writing a Story Write a story about winter. First, think about it. Next, fill in the planner. Then write the story. Last draw a picture.

Characters: _____   _____

(no more than 2)

Setting: _____

(where does story happen)

Problem to be solved: _____

(by main characters)

Events:

1.   _____

2.   _____

Ending: _____

Use your ideas to write a story:

_____

_____

_____

_____

Draw a picture here to go with your story.

Persuasive Writing

When you want to **persuade** someone to agree with your opinion or idea, you give reasons why your idea or opinion is a good one. Do you have an idea about something that you would really like to do? Now it is time to persuade your mom or dad using **persuasive writing**! Pick an idea below or think one up.

Ideas: get a pet   go to the park   buy some ice cream

Opinion: (e.g., I want to go to the zoo.)

_____

_____

_____

Two reasons or arguments to convince mom or dad that this is a good idea: (e.g., 1. I will get fresh air. 2. I want to learn about animals because I hope to be a vet when I grow up.)

1._____

_____

2._____

_____

Conclusion: (Rewrite opinion in different words. e.g., Going to the zoo will be fun and help me learn new things.)

_____

_____

Good luck!

Journal Writing

What is your favourite T.V. show? Write about it, including the title of the show, the names of the people in it, a funny scene, and what you like about it.

Days and Months Word Search

Find the days of the week and the months of the year in the word search. Print each one on a line below as you find it.

Days of the Week

_____

_____

_____

_____

_____

_____

```
Y W D A E Y A D S E U T E F
R R V D E C E M B E R C O D
U F E B R U A R Y R A Y R M
H R A A Y W E D N E S D A Y
M D D O Y R E B M E V O N F
O R T S U G U A J U L Y U B
R N M R E B M E T P E S E E
Y A D I R F Y A D S R U H T
E D S U Y A D N U S T U M A
J E A Y E N U J A N U A R Y
E Y S U E E Y A D R U T A S
Y A M O C T O B E R F J R Y
Y M A R C H M O N D A Y D H
Y T F A D Y A P R I L R R Y
```

Months of the Year

_____   _____

_____   _____

_____   _____

_____   _____

_____   _____

Solutions

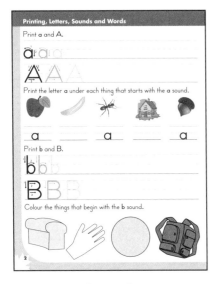

Page 2

Printing, Letters, Sounds and Words

Print a and A.

a a a
A A A

Print the letter a under each thing that starts with the a sound.

a   a   a

Print b and B.

b b b
B B B

Colour the things that begin with the b sound.

Page 3

Printing, Letters, Sounds and Words

Print c and C.

c c c
C C C

Circle the things that start with the c sound.

Print d and D.

d d d
D D D

Find these d words.

duck
dog
door
day
doll
do

d	d	d	o	g
o	a	u	u	g
o	y	c	c	o
r	a	k	w	o
d	o	l	l	d

Page 4

Printing, Letters, Sounds and Words

Print e and E.

e e e
E E E

Unscramble the letters to spell words that begin with the letter e.

sgeg   lfe   aet   eey   rae

eggs   elf   eat   eye   ear

Print f and F.

f f f
F F F

Colour the things that begin with the f sound.

Page 5

Printing, Letters, Sounds and Words

Print g and G.

g g g
G G G

Draw a line from the g in the middle to each thing that starts with the g sound. One is done for you.

Print h and H.

h h h
H H H

Circle the things that begin with the h sound.

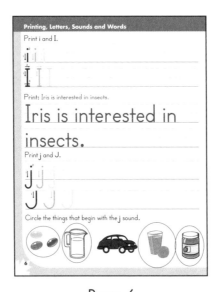

Page 6

Printing, Letters, Sounds and Words

Print i and I.

i i i
I I I

Print: Iris is interested in insects.

Iris is interested in insects.

Print j and J.

j j j
J J J

Circle the things that begin with the j sound.

Page 7

Printing, Letters, Sounds and Words

Print k and K.

k k k
K K K

Draw a line from the k in the middle to each thing that starts with the k sound.

Print l and L.

l l l
L L L

Circle the things that begin with the l sound.

Page 8

Printing, Letters, Sounds and Words

Print m and M.

m m m
M M M

Draw 3 things that start with the m sound.

Print n and N.

n n n
N N N

Unscramble the letters to spell words that start with the n sound.

stne   lain   tsun   etn   enni

nest   nail   nuts   net   nine

Page 9

Printing, Letters, Sounds and Words

Print o and O.

o o o
O O O

Print: Olivia opens oranges on her own.

Olivia opens oranges on her own.

Print p and P.

p p p
P P P

Colour the pictures that begin with the p sound.

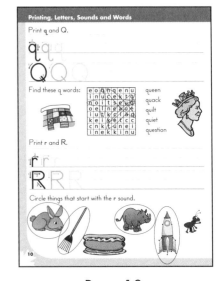

Page 10

Printing, Letters, Sounds and Words

Print q and Q.

q q q
Q Q Q

Find these q words:

e	o	q	n	q	e	n	u
i	n	u	c	k	t	q	a
n	o	i	t	s	e	u	q
i	u	t	k	c	i	a	g
k	e	k	e	c	c	c	
c	n	k	t	q	n	e	i
i	n	e	k	k	i	n	u

queen
quack
quilt
quiet
question

Print r and R.

r r r
R R R

Circle things that start with the r sound.

60

Solutions

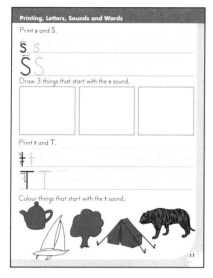

Page 11

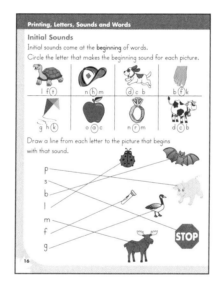

Page 13

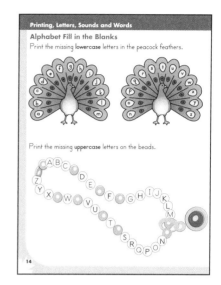

Page 14

Page 15

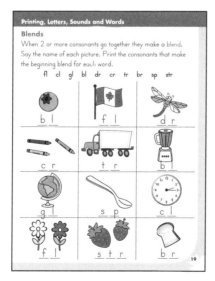

Page 16

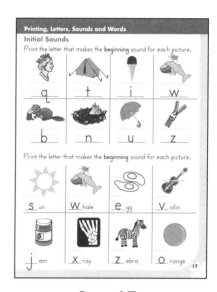

Page 17

Page 18

Page 19

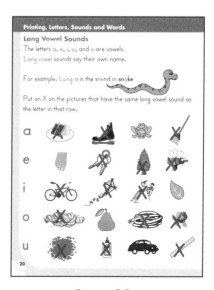

Page 20

61

Solutions

Page 21

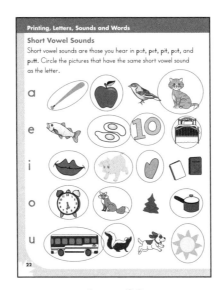

Page 22

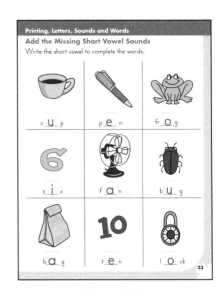

Page 23

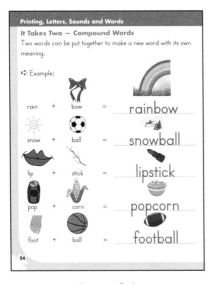

Page 24

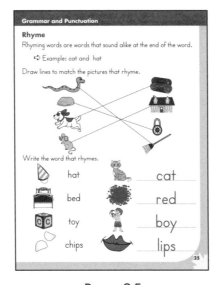

Page 25

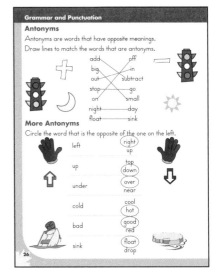

Page 26

Page 27

Page 28

Page 29

Solutions

Page 30

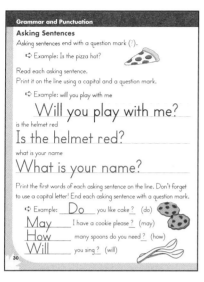

Grammar and Punctuation

Asking Sentences

Asking sentences end with a question mark (?).

↪ Example: Is the pizza hot?

Read each asking sentence.
Print it on the line using a capital and a question mark.

↪ Example: will you play with me

Will you play with me?

is the helmet red

Is the helmet red?

what is your name

What is your name?

Print the first words of each asking sentence on the line. Don't forget to use a capital letter! End each asking sentence with a question mark.

↪ Example: Do you like cake ? (do)

May I have a cookie please ? (may)

How many spoons do you need ? (how)

Will you sing ? (will)

Page 31

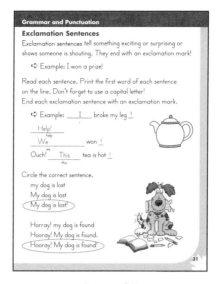

Grammar and Punctuation

Exclamation Sentences

Exclamation sentences tell something exciting or surprising or shows someone is shouting. They end with an exclamation mark!

↪ Example: I won a prize!

Read each sentence. Print the first word of each sentence on the line. Don't forget to use a capital letter!
End each exclamation sentence with an exclamation mark.

↪ Example: I broke my leg !

Help! help

We won !

Ouch! This tea is hot ! this

Circle the correct sentence.
my dog is lost
My dog is lost
(My dog is lost!)

Horray! my dog is found
Hooray! My dog is found
(Hooray! My dog is found!)

Page 32

Grammar and Punctuation

Complete the final punctuation. Use . ? or !
1. How old are you ?
2. I like to eat chocolate ice cream .
3. My favourite food is pizza .
4. What did you do on your vacation ?
5. How fast did you run ?
6. My dog can play catch with me !
7. I got an A on my last math test !
8. Does your teacher give you homework ?
9. The weather today is sunny and bright .
10. I want to have a fish for a pet .
11. Who is your best friend ?
12. My friend Mei Lei and I like to play soccer .
13. We won first prize !

Imagine you went to a birthday party.
Make up 2 telling sentences about the party.

1. _____

2. _____

Page 33

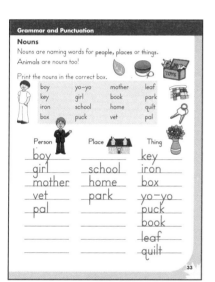

Grammar and Punctuation

Nouns

Nouns are naming words for people, places or things. Animals are nouns too!

Print the nouns in the correct box.

boy   yo-yo   mother   leaf
key   girl   book   park
iron   school   home   quilt
box   puck   vet   pal

Person	Place	Thing
boy	school	key
girl	home	iron
mother	park	box
vet		yo-yo
pal		puck
		book
		leaf
		quilt

Page 34

Grammar and Punctuation

Verbs

Verbs are action words that tell what someone or something does.

sits   jumps   reaches   splash   waves   swim

1. The kids swim laps together.
2. The boy jumps into the pool.
3. The woman waves to the girl.
4. The boys splash in the water.
5. The girl reaches for her goggles.
6. A boy sits on the side.

Page 35

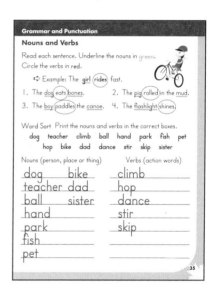

Grammar and Punctuation

Nouns and Verbs

Read each sentence. Underline the nouns in green.
Circle the verbs in red.

↪ Example: The girl (rides) fast.

1. The dog eats bones.   2. The pig rolled in the mud.
3. The boy paddles the canoe.   4. The flashlight shines.

Word Sort Print the nouns and verbs in the correct boxes.

dog   teacher   climb   ball   hand   park   fish   pet
hop   bike   dad   dance   stir   skip   sister

Nouns (person, place or thing)	Verbs (action words)
dog bike	climb
teacher dad	hop
ball sister	dance
hand	stir
park	skip
fish	
pet	

Page 36

Grammar and Punctuation

Adjectives

Adjectives are describing words. Read the describing words to figure out what the object is.

↪ Example: small cute soft
It is a puppy.

sun   zebra   ball   ice cream

hot yellow bright   It is a sun .
green round bouncy   It is a ball .
tasty cold hard   It is a ice cream .
striped black white   It is a zebra .

List two adjectives to describe each picture.

smelly   slipper
furry   wet

Answers will vary

Page 37

Grammar and Punctuation

Adjectives

Adjectives make a sentence more interesting.
Add describing words.

Answers will vary

1. A green frog is sitting on a warm rock.

2. The young boy likes to cook sweet marshmallows.

3. The soft rabbit hops on the green grass.

4. The old porcupine walks slowly.

5. Six little ants sit on the rough logs.

Page 38

Grammar and Punctuation

Sentences

Read the sentence. Follow the directions.

Ali scored a goal today.

1. Underline the word "scored."
2. Circle the word that tells what Ali scored.
3. Put an X on the word that tells who scored a goal.
4. Put a box around when Ali scored a goal.
5. Draw a picture of Ali scoring a goal.

Solutions

Grammar and Punctuation

Sentences

Put the words in the correct order. Print the sentence on the line. Start with a capital letter. End with a period.

slow is snail a

A snail is slow.

music nice plays man the

The man plays nice music.

swims the the in loon lake

The loon swims in the lake.

map the check let's

Let's check the map.

skip to I love

I love to skip.

Page 39

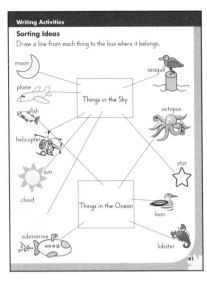

Writing Activities

Sorting Ideas

Draw a line from each thing to the box where it belongs.

moon, plane, fish, helicopter, sun, cloud, submarine — Things in the Sky

seagull, octopus, star, loon, lobster — Things in the Ocean

Page 41

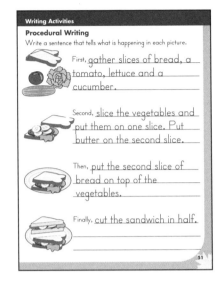

Writing Activities

Procedural Writing

Write a sentence that tells what is happening in each picture.

First, gather slices of bread, a tomato, lettuce and a cucumber.

Second, slice the vegetables and put them on one slice. Put butter on the second slice.

Then, put the second slice of bread on top of the vegetables.

Finally, cut the sandwich in half.

Page 51

Writing Activities

Read the sentences. What comes first? Put numbers beside the other sentences to show the order they happen.

I go to school. 5
I get dressed. 2
I wake up. 1
I brush my teeth. 4
I eat breakfast. 3

First, next, and last are words that tell the order of what happened in a story. Finish each sentence to tell the order of what happened in the pictures.

First, I planted a seed.

Next, I watered it.

Last, the flower grew.

Page 52

Writing Activities

Days and Months Word Search

Find the days of the week and the months of the year in the word search. Print each one on a line below as you find it.

Days of the Week

Monday
Tuesday
Wednesday
Thursday
Friday
Saturday
Sunday

```
Y W D A E Y A D S E U T D E F
R R V D E C E M B E R C O D
U F E B R U A R Y R A Y R M
H R A A Y W E D N E S D A Y
M D D O Y R E B M E V O N F
O R T S U G U A J U L Y U B
R N M R E B M E T P E S E E
Y A D I R F Y A D S R U H T
E D S U Y A D N U S T U M A
J E A Y E N U J A N U A R Y
E Y S U E E Y A D R U T A S
Y A M O C T O B E R J R Y
Y M A R C H M O N D A Y D H
Y T F A D Y A P R I L R R Y
```

Months of the Year

January   July
February   August
March   September
April   October
May   November
June   December

Page 59